A Teacher's Source Book for Mathematics in Classes 1–5

MAKING MATHS MEANINGFUL

A Teacher's Source Book for Mathematics in Classes 1–5

Jamie York,
Nettie Fabrie and Wim Gottenbos

Floris
Books

First published in the United States of America
by Jamie York Press, Boulder, CO in 2009
www.JamieYorkPress.com
First published in the UK in 2017 by Floris Books
adapted from the 2016 American edition

MIX
Paper from
responsible sources
FSC® C013604

British Library CIP Data available
ISBN 978-178250-430-6
Printed in Great Britain
by CPI Group (UK) Ltd, Croydon

Contents

Introduction

The maths tightrope

In teaching mathematics, perhaps like no other subject, we find ourselves walking a tightrope. If we step a bit to one side, a sizable portion of the class becomes perplexed and overwhelmed. If we correct ourselves to the other side, the quicker students get bored and the class as a whole doesn't progress enough. For many teachers, each step along this tightrope brings up unpleasant memories from their own childhood.

As Waldorf teachers, we are aware that the teaching of maths is more than just an intellectual exercise. We engage the will of the students as we use movement and rhythmical exercises to teach the times tables. Through appropriate stories, we engage the feeling realm of the children and spark their interest in maths. Rudolf Steiner, the founder of the first Waldorf school, spoke of the importance of 'permeating the soul with mathematics in the right way' and how a healthy relationship to mathematics can benefit the student's later spiritual development.

Certainly, maths in a Waldorf school is viewed differently and taught differently. Yet, the problems we face are often the same as in the mainstream. All too often, a class enters middle school with many of the students weak in maths and saying, 'I'm bad at maths, and I hate it.' Why is this so? How can we do better?

About this book

While this book is intended for someone currently teaching maths in lower classes of a Waldorf school, the material presented here can be effectively used by any teacher wishing to bring meaningful, age-appropriate maths to their students.

Although we have attempted to address many of the issues that we feel are important, we must acknowledge that there is much more to teaching maths than what is found within the covers of a book. Neither this nor any other book can be a substitute for a proper teacher-training programme, where much of the fundamental and necessary philosophy, pedagogical basis, and teaching technique are covered.

This book, perhaps, focuses more on aspects of mathematics teaching that the authors feel are often in need of improvement in Waldorf schools.

A word of caution

The authors hope that the contents of this book will be helpful to teachers and bring to consciousness some aspects of maths teaching that may otherwise not surface. We hope that this book will generate thought and discussion. It should not be viewed as a recipe for teaching mathematics in a Waldorf school. Indeed there is no such recipe. This book is merely a resource that reflects the opinions of the authors. There are other opinions as well that may also be called 'Waldorf'.

The reader (presumably a teacher) should not simply follow instructions or carry out a plan just because it is stated in this book. As always, it is the teacher's job to develop an inner sense of what is right at a particular moment for the class and to create an effective lesson. It is ultimately the teacher's love and creativity that will bring the material alive for the students. No book can give this to the teacher.

Other books and website

The website *www.JamieYorkPress.com* has full-colour photos of children's main lesson book pages, free downloads of a variety of practice sheets, and access to other resources related to *Making Maths Meaningful* books. You can also contact us there with questions and comments.

There may be occasions when the teacher knows it is time to do something different. Our *Fun with Puzzles, Games and More!* is intended as a resource for maths teachers in Classes Four to Twelve, in part to supplement the normal classroom material. It provides ideas for that 'something different'.

Additionally, there are books for middle school and upper school maths. *A Teacher's Source Books for Mathematics in Classes 6–8* as well as *Student Workbooks* for each of those classes are available from Floris Books. There are further books available from Jamie York Press in the United States.

Acknowledgements

The authors wish to thank the following people for their help in making this book possible: Marilyn Fox for ideas on Class Two place value; Grace Wang, Vienna Scheyer and Katja Kramers, students of the Seattle Waldorf school for sharing their beautiful maths main lesson books; Meike Gottenbos for helping with some drawings; and Ruud Luiten for technical support. And a very special thank you goes to Else Göttgens for the many wonderful discussions about child development we have had over the past 35 years.

Teaching Maths in Lower Classes

The challenge of teaching maths in the lower classes

Fear and stress

In this day and age, fear can have an influence over much of our lives, including our children's education. Teachers and parents are more worried than ever. 'What will happen if my child falls behind?' The pressure to get ahead has increased. Education has become a race. More advanced material at a younger age. More homework. More high stakes testing. More fear. More stress. Even independent schools are affected.

Stress and fear are not conducive to learning anything; they impair our students' ability to learn maths. We need to reduce fear and stress and create a calm, safe learning environment, which enables our students to achieve an inner state of calm contemplation. This creates a vessel in which learning maths is possible.

Avoiding struggle

Ironically, even though there are greater expectations for our children to learn more material and do more homework – all at a younger age – we don't want them to struggle. We want our children to be happy and successful. We live in an 'instant gratification' culture. If we want something to happen, we expect it quickly. And it should be easy. Our children should get As, be ahead of the others, and be comfortable.

The trouble is that learning maths usually isn't that quick and easy. It takes patience – patience on the part of the student, patience on the part of the teacher, and patience on the part of the parents. Working through struggle is an important part of learning maths – and is a great life lesson. One of our challenges as class teachers today is to create a safe environment – without fear and stress – in which our students can work through their difficulties. This is certainly no easy task. Wouldn't it be wonderful if all of our children could learn how to calmly face their challenges and develop confidence as they successfully work through their struggles?

What are the symptoms of our 'maths illness'?

Meaningless maths

What is society's view of maths? Maths is often not seen as meaningful in and of itself. A widespread belief is that 'good maths' must be practical and useful. It then follows that the main reason to study maths is that it can be useful for some other purpose or subject. All of these attitudes toward maths can make it challenging to teach in a meaningful way.

While we, the authors, believe that practical applications of maths can be helpful, we also feel that there is a higher purpose to learning maths (see *Principles of Waldorf education,* p. 13.)

The list

If people believe that maths should always be practical, then it stands to reason that skill development would become the primary focus. Over time this has degenerated into a horrifically long list of skills that are supposedly necessary for our children to move to the next level (middle school, upper school, or university). The list manages to put pressure on teachers at all levels of education. They fear that if they don't get through the entire list, then their students won't be prepared. We are led to believe that this list is getting longer and longer, and more and more daunting. Such an over-emphasis on skill development is boring or overwhelming (or both) for many students, and for the teacher as well.

We believe that basic skills are important, but the list of topics needed to move forward is not horrifically long; it is actually quite manageable (see *What skills are really needed?* p. 19). We also believe there is much more to maths than just learning skills. With so much emphasis going toward the mastery of a long list of skills, some of the more interesting aspects of mathematics become neglected.

Making maths procedural

The tendency in schools today is to spend far too much time on procedural skills at too young an age. Examples include borrowing in Class Two, long division in Class Three, and arithmetic with mixed numbers in Class Four. Each of these topics would probably be better introduced at least a full year later than what was just mentioned. But here's the real issue: by having too much of an emphasis on procedural skills at too young an age, the children experience maths as a collection of blind procedures, probably paving the way for maths anxiety or trauma. Even for those students who aren't traumatised by the blind procedures, it is likely that they will not have an understanding of what they are doing, and that later, in higher classes, they will have troubles when the mathematical concepts become more challenging.

For example, in the process of doing a borrowing problem, such as 72 – 58, many Class Two or Class Three pupils lose sight of the two numbers, 72 and 58. Instead they see columns of numbers: 7 minus 5, and 2 minus 8 (which is made possible through the trick of borrowing). Perhaps worst of all, they then lose sight of what subtraction really is; for them subtraction has become this blind procedure called 'borrowing'.

Likewise, in the process of doing a long division problem, students of Classes Three or Four forget that they are doing a division problem; they forget what division really is. And in the process of doing arithmetic with two mixed numbers (e.g. $8\frac{2}{3} + 5\frac{1}{2}$), the Class Four student sees six numbers (8, 2, 3, 5, 1, 2) placed in specific locations. The final answer is then just the end result of a series of steps or tricks. In such cases, much of the work with fractions ends up being a collection of tricks (see *Be aware of tricks!* p. 33) The student probably forgets that the problem had anything to do with fractions and may not truly understand what a fraction is.

We believe that such procedural skills may be introduced in the lower classes, but that an over-emphasis on these skills when children are too young often results in their losing the big picture, not understanding the concepts behind the procedure, and losing (or not developing) their sense of number. All of this increases the chance of children later becoming maths traumatised.

The big race

Today's society seems to picture education as a race. Programmes like 'No Child Left Behind' and 'Head Start' reinforce this image. The impression we are given is that getting ahead early translates into being ahead at the finish. We disagree.

Not only is there much more to a child's education than getting ahead, but pushing advanced material on young children (in Classes One to Four) does not translate into being ahead in the long run. In fact, such an approach usually results in

- 'dumbing-down' the material;
- teaching that is superficial, uninspirational and deadening; and
- overwhelming many of the students.

Instead, the best approach is to proceed slowly in the early classes, ensuring that the material is covered thoroughly, so that all of the students deeply absorb what is being brought to them. Then, after having built such a solid foundation, the children are set to really take off in middle and upper school. The best we can do in the lower classes, if we want our students to be strong when they graduate, is to give them a strong foundation in the fundamentals and engender a joy for learning.

Homework and reports

Homework and reports are topics that extend further than the maths classroom, but we feel that they are sufficiently important to mention here.*

The trend in education today is to give more and more homework at a younger and younger age. Many teachers want to prove to the parents in their class that the children are doing advanced work. Even Waldorf teachers are caving in to this pressure. It's not uncommon today for Class Three children to be given homework.

We question this trend. We feel that there should be no homework until Class Five, and, even then, it should be minimal. Any homework should help to create joy in learning. Children spend many hours in school. This is where they should learn to work hard. Children need a life outside school! At home they need to play, read, practise their musical instrument, do crafts, draw, paint, play board games,† take part in the household chores, and spend

---

* For further reading that questions the value of homework, see Alfie Kohn's book, *The Homework Myth.*

† See the Appendix, p. 111, for a list of games for lower school maths.

time with friends and family. To quote Rudolf Steiner:

> There is another thing to be considered. In the Waldorf School practically all the teaching takes place in the school itself. The burden of homework is lifted, for the children are given very little to do at home. Because all the work is done together with the teachers, the children's attitude is a quite remarkable one.*

It is often said that giving homework in the early classes helps to develop good work habits for later. This gives the impression that the best way to prepare children for the stressful burden of homework, which they will encounter in higher classes, is to have them experience this burden in the younger classes. In contrast, we feel that good homework habits can be developed in middle school, and even then, with a minimal amount of homework.

In a similar way, teachers now require the children to do written reports or essays. It seems that this comes from mainstream education where there is a desire to imitate an aspect of higher-level education (research papers). This gets watered down and brought to young children. Parents who are pushing for more academics may be pacified. But we feel that such reports have little pedagogical value and can even have a negative impact on children's enthusiasm for learning. We have similar concerns about book reports. Of course, there is nothing wrong with encouraging children to read a book at home. But forcing children to read a book that they may not be interested in, and then burdening them with writing a report on it, is likely to dampen their enthusiasm for reading.

Maths trauma

Many adults in our society are weak in maths and intimidated by it. Why does this happen? At what age did the maths trauma begin? At what age does a child start saying, 'I'm bad at maths'? While for some students maths trauma may not be apparent until adolescence, we believe that in most cases the root causes of maths trauma begin between Class Two and Class Four.†

Perhaps our single greatest task when teaching maths in the lower classes is to ensure that our students don't enter middle school maths traumatised. But this is no easy task!

Two ends of the spectrum

Too much too soon. Class teachers can be pressured by parents or colleagues to prove that their own class is strong at maths, doing advanced material, and ahead (or at least not behind) other classes. The teacher may or may not be conscious of this pressure, and much of this may be self-inflicted. Because of this pressure, the teacher is then inclined to move quickly through the material and go into too

---

* *Human Values in Education,* lecture of July 21, 1924.

† D.B. McLeod, Research on affect in mathematics education: A reconceptualization, pp. 575–96 in D.A. Grouws (ed.), *Handbook of Research on Mathematics Teaching and Learning.*

much depth with material when the students are too young. All of this will probably lose a good portion of the class, leaving them maths traumatised and thinking that they will never become good at maths. Such a class often enters middle school with a huge disparity between those who are good at maths (the 'fast students') and those who aren't good at maths (the 'slow students'), with few students in between (see *Avoiding the Great Divide* p. 34)

Maths deprivation. Don't mistake what has been said above as an argument to do as little maths as possible. If teachers avoid maths because they (or the students) find it unpleasant, or keep the maths too simple, then the class won't progress enough, and the students' sense of number and ability to 'think mathematically' will be underdeveloped. Such students will probably have difficulties in later years when they have a teacher who has higher expectations.

It's all about balance. We need to have (reasonably) high expectations of our students. Each student should be appropriately challenged in maths. Developing a sense for what is right for the class is an important part of the art of teaching.

Lack of independent, creative and flexible thinking

Certainly one of the ultimate goals of any educational system should be that its graduates can think independently, flexibly and creatively. Yet, we often hear from university professors and leaders in industry that today's education isn't able to adequately produce graduates who are good problem-solvers and can think creatively. Clearly, an approach to teaching maths that amounts to marching through a textbook and blindly memorising procedures is not likely to develop independent thinking.

Students are often given the impression that there is only one way to do a maths problem – that maths is rigid and inflexible. We need to instead look for opportunities to show that there are multiple ways to solve a problem, and elicit from our students their different ideas for doing a calculation or solving a problem. If we are successful with this in the younger classes, it can make it possible for our students to develop into independent and creative thinkers in high school and beyond (see also *Developing flexibility in thinking*, p. 34.)

Principles of Waldorf education

Waldorf education's principles and unique goals are drawn from Rudolf Steiner's insights into child development. What is listed here is an essential part of any Waldorf training programme for class teachers. Some of the most important principles are as follows:

Child development

It is important that all Waldorf teachers (from pre-kindergarten to Class Twelve) have a deep understanding of child development and the development of the human being in general.

Developmentally appropriate material

With this understanding of child development, the teacher can then become conscious of how something brought into the classroom affects the children developmentally. A central principle of Waldorf education is that the curriculum supports the development of the child. The right subject at the right time does this. For example, in Class Four, as children separate from the world, the unity of their surroundings falls apart. Therefore, at this time in the curriculum, we see this reflected in the introduction to fractions, where the whole number falls into many pieces. This process with fractions helps to support children through this transition in their life.

Working with the imagination

It is important for the teacher to work with enlivening images and pictures through the children's imaginations rather than using dead concepts and judgments.

Teaching from the whole to the part

By proceeding from the whole to the parts, we divide or restructure the whole into multiple parts. For example, imagine that we have 12 chestnuts and we ask the students to divide these chestnuts. There are many possibilities for dividing the whole of 12 into parts.* If we go from the parts to the whole (for instance, asking, 'What is 10 + 2?') we have only one possible answer. This is a materialistic gesture. If we instead go from the whole to the parts, we have a more social gesture – a 'giving-away' gesture.

The conscious use of forgetting

We might think that if we were successful in teaching children, they would always remember what they were taught; if they forget what they were taught, then it must be a sign that we have failed. But this is not so. Forgetting is an important part of learning.† After teaching something new to children, we should then let it go. It 'goes to sleep' in the children and works on them subconsciously. Then, after some time, we review – bringing the old topic back and deepening it. The children will have forgotten what they had previously known, but then, during this review process, they will quickly remember it all, and have a new, deeper understanding of the material.

The pedagogical law

As a central tenet of Waldorf education, the teacher educates each of the students' (finer) bodies by working out of their higher body. In kindergarten and early childhood education, young children are largely working on the development of their physical body. Therefore, the teacher works out of their etheric body while working with imitation. Prior to the teenage years, it is the teacher's astral body that aids

---

* Rudolf Steiner, *Renewal of Education*, lecture of May 5, 1920 (Synthesis and Analysis in Human Nature and Education).

† Rudolf Steiner, *The Being of Man and His Future Evolution*, lecture of Nov 2, 1908 (Forgetting).

the development of the students' etheric. After that, it is the teacher's I (or self) that helps to develop a healthy astral body in the students.*

Educating the 'freed etheric body'

During the child's first seven years, the etheric forces were used to shape the physical body. With the change of teeth, some of these forces are then freed up and available for the learning process. The education of this freed etheric in the child starts in Class One. What has been developed unconsciously in the first seven years will come to blossom in the next seven years through our work in the classroom. After age seven we can begin to work with the freed etheric forces and nourish the astral body. What we are trying to cultivate is memory, lasting habits, temperaments, lasting inclinations, and enduring desires.†

Let's be clear what we mean when we say we need to work on the child's etheric body. When most Waldorf teachers think of working with the children's etheric bodies, they tend to think mostly of rhythm. The teachers then tend to spend more time and energy with the rhythmical activities in the lesson than work-ing to strengthen the memory forces.‡ Every morning in a Waldorf school, we can hear many rhythmical activities, mainly done by the teacher, where the whole class follows at will. In these cases, the children often don't work enough individually with the material.

However, working with the child's freed etheric body actually has more to do with memory, habits and imagination. 'Fully conscious repetition cultivates the true will's impulse.' Instead of just counting the beats by ones every day, the teacher should also work with the students counting the windows, the eyes, the noses, the fingers, the legs of the chairs, etc. 'A more unconscious repetition cultivates feeling.'§

Review and practice

In Waldorf pedagogy, the word 'review' is used in two ways: first, daily review, which helps the child recall what was done during the previous day's lesson, and secondly, review of material that was covered some time ago. Both are an important part of the learning process. Unfortunately, both are often skipped or done ineffectively, even in Waldorf schools.

Regarding the first meaning of the word 'review', Rudolf Steiner emphasised in his lectures, *The Foundations of Human Experience,* the importance of how the teacher must

---

* Rudolf Steiner, *The Education of the Child in the Light of Anthroposophy,* discusses the birth of the human being's four bodies. This essay of 1909 was based on lectures given eleven years before the start of the first Waldorf School.

† Rudolf Steiner, *The Destinies of Individuals and of Nations,* lecture of April 20, 1915 (The Etheric Being in the Physical Human Being). Also J. Bockemühl (ed.), *Towards a Phenomenology of the Etheric World,* (pp. 217–35).

‡ Rudolf Steiner, Memory, Chapter 6 in *Persephone: Education and Teaching as Preventative Medicine,* Medical Section, Dornach, Switzerland, 2006.

§ Rudolf Steiner, *The Foundations of Human Experience,* lecture of August 23, 1919.

be conscious of using the child's time of sleep as part of the learning process. This is a central tenet of Waldorf pedagogy. Therefore the teacher must review – bring back into the child's imagination – the material from the previous day. In doing this, the teacher should review the lesson from the previous day by using different examples. For instance, in Class One, we might regroup 12 children, and then the next day during the review we might regroup 12 chairs. Then we can go further by working with a new number.

The second meaning of the word 'review' relates to the word 'practise'; the children should practise material from the current main lesson block (when the class is having a maths block), previous blocks, and previous classes.* In today's culture, there seems to be less patience for review and practice. Teachers today are often hesitant to have their students practise very much because they feel that it isn't interesting for the students. In contrast, we believe that review and practice are vitally important for successful maths lessons.

However, keep in mind that it may be best to allow new material that has just been introduced in one block to 'sleep' until the next maths block. This new material is not mentioned again until the next maths block, at which point it is reviewed and practised. Once that maths block has been concluded (and the class is in a non-maths block), this material (from two blocks ago) can then be occasionally worked into the daily 10 minutes of maths practice time.

Students can only learn maths skills through adequate and systematic review and practice. The teacher needs to ensure that the students review and practise both the new material and topics covered in previous blocks. An old teacher's motto states that for a student to learn something permanently it should be reviewed the next day, the next week, the next month, and the next year. That is systematic review!

However, be sure that there is joy during maths practice time. The problems should be interesting; there should always be something new to discover.

Teaching economically

In a Waldorf school, we are able to teach fewer hours of maths than what is done in the mainstream, and still our students do fine and usually are ahead of students from other schools. We teach economically. This is possible for a number of reasons. First of all, the Waldorf class teacher stays with the class for several years, which enables the teacher to develop a deeper relationship with their students and to better know the students' strengths, weaknesses, and how they learn. In a Waldorf school, we are doing much more than teaching skills. We develop capacities in our students. Starting in the early classes, we work on developing the students' observation skills, which allows them to more easily relate one situation

* A main lesson in a Waldorf school takes place first thing in the morning for about 1½ to 2 hours. A variety of activities are done during this time, but the subject of the main lesson changes every three to four weeks.

to another, and thereby more easily solve a new maths problem. These are just some of the reasons that Waldorf education stands out!

A higher purpose

Rudolf Steiner spoke about how mathematics is a training in sense-free thinking. He also spoke about how the proper teaching of maths is an important part of the students' moral and spiritual development. By developing mathematical capacities in our students, we are helping to lay the foundation for the students' spiritual development later in life.

> The student of mathematics must get rid of all arbitrary thinking and follow purely the demands of thought. In thinking in this way, the laws of the spiritual world flow into him. This regulated thinking leads to the most spiritual truths.*

The Waldorf class teacher

All teachers have a tremendous responsibility to oversee the development of the children in their class. Additionally, all Waldorf teachers have a great deal of freedom in deciding what to bring into the classroom. They do not rely on textbooks; instead each child creates his own book for every main lesson.

It is important that we, as Waldorf teachers, are the authors of what comes into the classroom. It needs to be clear to us why we do what we do. We shouldn't just blindly do something because it's what everyone else does. We need to feel it's right for the students in front of us. In this way we take ownership of the curriculum.

Teacher's study

As teaching staff, we need to study anthroposophy. The teaching of mathematics is one of the instruments that we use to aid the children in their development. Studying child development (e.g. temperaments, polarities and the senses) gives us a deeper understanding of the children and helps inspire us in our maths lessons. This is an essential part of being a Waldorf teacher.

Imagination and maths

In today's society, imagination is associated largely with fantasy and not viewed as very 'useful'. It is therefore not surprising that in mainstream education, the development of children's imagination can be considered unimportant. In contrast, Waldorf education holds that the development of imagination is a central aspect of developing the whole child.

Until the age of 13 or 14, children think mainly in pictures and images. If we want these younger children to work willingly, images will motivate them. If we want them to learn eagerly, then pictures will entice them to listen and remember. When we prepare our lessons, we should ask ourselves: 'Have I found the proper images for what I want them to learn?'†

---

* Rudolf Steiner, *Spiritual Ground of Education*, lecture of Aug 21, 1922.

† Else Göttgens, *Waldorf Education in Practice: Exploring How Children Learn in the Lower Grades*.

In terms of the teaching of maths, imagination can be woven into the lessons, not just by telling compelling stories, but also by showing students that maths is a fascinating and creative human endeavor. In this way, maths can be a springboard for thinking flexibly and creatively.

> *Imagination is more important than knowledge. Knowledge is limited. Imagination encircles the world.* (Albert Einstein)

Will our children be prepared?

Preparation for middle school, upper school and university maths

Often we hear parents who worry about their children's maths, say, 'Will our children be prepared?' This certainly is a fair question. We may then ask, 'Prepared for what?' Usually the anxiety is regarding preparation for the next step – whether this next step is middle school, upper school, or university. And today, this anxiety about 'being prepared' seems to be with children at a younger and younger age.

It is an interesting exercise to ask a group of parents who have this question – and perhaps the anxiety as well – what they think it would look like to have their children well prepared in maths for the 'next step'. Surprisingly, when brought in this way, parents won't usually speak of the necessity for their child to learn a long list of maths skills, nor will they say how important it is that their child be ahead of other students.

We believe that there are four critical ingredients that our children need in order to be prepared for their next step in their maths education – be it middle school, high school, or university.

Enthusiasm for learning

Enthusiasm and love of learning maths will probably take any student a long way. No matter how good their skills are, no parent or teacher wants their child to be apathetic about learning.

Study skills

The term 'study skills' is broad; it includes organisation, work habits, etc. In the lower classes, we prepare and plant the seeds for the work in the higher classes by developing good habits, which includes ensuring that the students complete their work, that their work is well organised, readable, and that they show interest and take pride in it. Along these lines, we should ask, 'Have they learned how to learn, and do they have confidence in their abilities to learn new material?'

Higher level thinking

All too often in today's world, students graduate from high school and university unable to think for themselves. Their thinking, even when doing maths, is largely imitative; they can do maths problems as long as they have seen something similar before. As Waldorf educators, our goal is to have students graduate school who can think flexibly, creatively, and independently. We want our students to be able to think for themselves, think analytically, and we hope that their thinking is heartfelt and imbued with imagination. Once again, this starts in the lower classes. If we don't start here, it is unlikely that we will reach this goal in the upper classes.

Basic maths skills
Yes, skills are important. If the students don't master the basic skills, they will not feel confident in moving forward. However, the list of necessary skills needed for the next step isn't as daunting as we might be led to believe…

What skills are really needed?

Maths educators often agree that there is too much of an emphasis on procedural skills in maths education today. They say that we need to find more time to develop problem-solving skills (something that begins in the lower classes, but becomes more important later) and creative thinking capabilities. Yet, many teachers complain that there is never enough time for these 'extras'. We can begin to feel that there is an overwhelming amount of material that the students must learn, and, if they don't learn it all, they won't be ready for the next step. As we stated above, the actual list of necessary skills is relatively short. The following lists are simply intended as benchmarks in two-year intervals.

Skills needed by the end of Class Four
Arithmetic facts learned 'by heart'
By the end of Class Three , the students should know all of the arithmetic facts (including addition, subtraction, multiplication and division) by heart. Work in Class Four simply reinforces what they learned earlier (see *Learning the arithmetic facts,* p. 23).

Sense of number
Teaching the children so that they develop a sense of number is very important, but is not something that comes easily or can be taught directly (see *Developing a sense of number,* p. 25).

What about the rest of the skills? Our answer to this question may appear either shocking or pleasantly surprising. Procedural skills do not need to be mastered before Class Five. The key word here is 'mastered'. Of course, the students should be introduced to many of these procedural skills before Class Five (see also *Making maths procedural,* p. 10).

Skills needed by the end of Class Six
Many of the skills mentioned below may have been introduced earlier, but should be mastered (after a brief review) by the end of Class Six.

The four processes
This includes vertical arithmetic (i.e. carrying, borrowing, long multiplication, and long division), which was no doubt introduced in the early classes, but may not be fully mastered until Class Five by most students. For more

complicated problems, some students may not achieve full mastery until the end of Class Six.

Fractions and decimals
Fractions are introduced in Class Four, but thorough practice of fraction skills only starts in Class Five. It will take much of Class Six before many students will be completely comfortable with fractions. Decimals (i.e. decimal fractions) should be a fairly easy step if the groundwork with fractions has been laid adequately.

Measurement
Measurement is introduced in Class Three as a main lesson, and reviewed and practised in Class Four. The students should have mastery over simple conversion problems (e.g. how many metres is 5.8 cm?). Estimating measurement is also an important skill to be learned.

Estimating
For example, estimating that 573×42 is approximately 24,000.

Skills needed by the end of Class Eight
Many of the skills mentioned below may have been introduced earlier, but should be mastered (after a brief review) by the end of Class Eight.

Percents
Percents should be briefly introduced in Class Six, reviewed and furthered in Class Seven (but still kept quite simple!), and then really developed and solidified in Class Eight.

Ratios and proportions
Ratios and proportions are an important theme in Class Seven and Eighth maths.

Basic algebra
This includes signed numbers, formulas, and basic equations (e.g. $8 - x + 3 = 2x - 7 - 9x$).

Measurement
This includes basic problems with area (e.g. of a circle) and volume (e.g. of a cube).

Dimensional analysis
This mostly consists of conversions between the imperial and the metric system (e.g. 5.2 cm is how many inches?). Students should be able to use a conversion table to help with these calculations.

The major themes for maths
Classes 1–4: Developing a sense of number
These early classes are not about the mastery of written procedural skills (e.g. vertical arithmetic and calculations with fractions), even though these procedures were introduced in Classes Three and Four. Classes One to Four are about developing a sense of number. Written procedural skills can be firmed up starting in Class Five.

Classes 5–6: Consolidating skills
In Classes Five and Six, we consolidate skills that were introduced in earlier classes and develop mastery with written procedural skills, such as doing arithmetic problems in vertical form (i.e. carrying, borrowing, long multiplication,

and long division) and doing arithmetic with fractions. Class Six is also about seeing the interconnectedness in maths (e.g. the relationship between fractions, decimals, percents and division).

Classes 7–9: Developing abstract thinking
This is also the time to develop the students' confidence in their own thinking. Class Seven is the 'eye of the needle' – it is often then that the student's relationship to maths is determined for the upper school and beyond.

Classes 10–12: Developing logical, analytical, synthetic thinking
If all of the groundwork has been properly laid, then this is when we truly see the fruits of all the earlier hard work that has been put into the child's education. Academics, 'real maths', and independent thinking can all really take off at the end of the upper school as the student begins to find their own identity and destiny.

Preparation for life
Of course, there is much more to education than preparing our students for maths in middle school, upper school, or university. Patrick Bassett, former head of the (American) National Association of Independent Schools, asks the question: 'What skills and values are necessary for students to succeed and prosper in the twenty-first century?'*

---

* Patrick Bassett, Demonstrations of Learning for 21st Century Schools, *Independent Perspective* (Journal), Fall 2009.

In order to answer this question, Bassett refers to several sources, including a Harvard-based study; the government's commission on education; a think tank for higher education; the academic testing industry; public opinion surveys; Tony Wagner's *Seven Survival Skills*; and Howard Gardner's book, *Five Minds for the Future*. What Bassett finds is a surprisingly high degree of congruence between these very different sources.

In the end, Bassett's own list of skills and values needed for the twenty-first century is:

- *Character.* This includes qualities such as self-discipline, empathy, integrity, resilience, courage, etc.
- *Creativity.* It goes without saying that a strength of an arts-integrated curriculum is developing creativity in its students. But it is also important that our education helps to develop creative thinking as well. Later in life, this quality manifests itself as adaptability and developing an entrepreneurial spirit.
- *Critical thinking.* This includes problem solving, the ability to analyse information (filtering, analysis, and synthesis), questioning what you are 'told' in the media, and thinking for yourself.
- *Communication.* This is more than just reading and writing. Bassett is very clear that the emphasis here is public speaking. Yet, in today's world of media and computer screens, children (and adults!) are losing their abilities to speak articulately. Think of how beneficial it is to have the students, year after year, stand in front of an audience

and speak – be it in a dramatic play, or at an all-school assembly.

- *Teaming.* The ability for people to work together productively and collaboratively has become more important than ever. And today's youth loves working in groups!
- *Leadership.* Today, perhaps more than ever, the world is in need of inspirational leaders who have strong values, and the courage and will to 'stand up for the good'.

We believe that the above six skills and values speak for the strength (and need!) of Waldorf education.

In the maths classroom

Two types of topics: skills and mathematical experiences

As teachers, it is only natural that our own education deeply influences our view of mathematics. For most of us, our formal maths education worked largely like this: the teacher explained a new concept; the teacher gave us examples of solving problems with this new topic; we practised the new problems for homework; after some time, we were tested; and, at some point later, the topic was reviewed. In spite of much work on teaching methods in mathematics, and many experiments with mathematics curriculum, this model for teaching remains prevalent today from primary school to secondary school. In many cases this model for teaching maths is both appropriate and effective; in many cases it is not.

This method for teaching maths is com-pletely focused on skills. It is probably most useful in Classes Seven to Nine. In earlier years, such a skills-based approach should be used sparingly. In later years (upper school and beyond), students should be encouraged to think more on their own and not just imitate their teacher.

As teachers, we sometimes think that the students are supposed to 'learn' everything that we teach – that everything should be learned, tested, and retained. However, that's not true. It can be helpful to consider that maths topics can be divided into two categories: skills (i.e. material that needs to be mastered) and mathematical experiences.

Skills (a topic that needs to be mastered)

Here the teacher needs to create a dance between introducing, deepening, practising, sleeping, and reviewing. The bigger the topic (e.g. fractions), the greater the number of times it needs to be put to sleep, and then later reviewed. It is quite typical to introduce a skills topic one year, but not to have the students reach mastery until the next year, or the year after.

Mathematical experiences

With a 'pure' mathematical experience, there is often no expectation that the students remember the topic or learn it as a skill. Examples of such topics include puzzle problems, 'wonder of number' topics, number bases (Class Eight), and a variety of geometric topics. We teach these topics because they stretch our students' minds, teaching them to think mathematically, and they engender enthusiasm and wonder for maths.

And, of course, we should acknowledge that many topics can be considered a mix of skills and mathematical experiences.

Learning the arithmetic facts

Far too often, students going into Class Six are too slow with arithmetical procedures (e.g. long division, multiplication) simply because they don't know their arithmetic facts.* This should not happen.

Knowing the arithmetic facts has nothing to do with how 'smart' a student is. In reality, a lack of confidence often causes students to do poorly in maths during their middle school and upper school years. This lack of confidence often starts from them not knowing their multiplication facts, which makes them think that they must be bad at maths, and in the end it can turn into a self-fulfilling prophecy.

There is a fairly narrow window – the centre of which is Class Three – for learning the arithmetic facts. It is much more difficult to learn these facts by heart after Class Four.

So how can we reach our goal of having all of our students learn their arithmetic facts by

heart by the end of Class Three? The real key to achieving this goal is working systematically and creatively with the children starting in Class One. To help in this effort, we have prepared arithmetic facts practice sheets that can be used in Class Three, and have also prepared practice sheets for review and increasing speed for Classes Four and Five. These sheets can be downloaded free from *www.JamieYorkPress.com*.

For more details, be sure to read the following two sections of this book:
A step-by-step progression for the arithmetic facts (in the Appendix, pp. 111f).
Arithmetic facts practice sheets (p. 75).

Word problems

At times, word problems are held up as being more important than they really are. Some say that word problems show how maths can be useful in the real world, and that word problems help to develop problem-solving abilities. Neither is necessarily true. In truth, many students (especially in the upper classes) quickly learn to hate word problems; they shut down as soon as they see one.

There are many different types of word problems, and many levels. It is helpful to keep in mind that the analytical thinking abilities needed for true problem solving only really blossom toward the end of the upper school.

Our point here is not to say that word problems should be avoided until the upper school. Word problems should be brought into the classroom, starting in Class One, through

---

* Throughout this book, the term 'arithmetic facts' refers to all of the basic facts that should be learned by heart, including the addition facts (up to $18 = 9 + 9$), the corresponding subtraction facts, the multiplication facts up to the 12 times table (of course, out of order), and the corresponding division facts.

stories and images. But we should be very careful! We need to keep in mind the pedagogical purpose of word problems. Word problems can help students see the interconnectedness of language – how English can be used to express a maths problem. Word problems – if well chosen – can show how mathematics can appear in our everyday lives. We need to carefully consider how to bring them to the class in a way that isn't traumatising. Keep it simple, and make it fun!

Mental arithmetic

In our modern technological world, it may seem that the ability to work with numbers in your head is no longer necessary. We strongly disagree. Mental arithmetic* is an important skill to be developed from Class One up through middle school. If practised regularly in the classroom, mental arithmetic strengthens the students' sense of number, challenges their memory, increases their ability to focus, and develops general cognitive capacities. The use of calculators weakens the students' ability to do mental arithmetic. We therefore discourage the use of calculators before Class Eight.

Mental arithmetic can be worked on in a variety of ways, including orally with the whole class, or individually on paper (e.g. arithmetic facts practice sheets). It can be used for practising skills (arithmetic facts in Class Three or Four, or simple fraction practice in Class Five),

or it can focus more on simply developing the ability to work with numbers in your head. As a guideline, mental arithmetic should be practised daily for 10 minutes or less. Examples of mental arithmetic calculations are:

Arithmetic facts
Before Class Four, much of mental arithmetic may consist of practising the basic arithmetic facts.

Number journeys
For example, what is 5 plus 8, minus 3, times 6, divided by 2, divided by 5? Be careful, though – weaker students may give up on number journeys.

'Halfway' problems
These can be done for different class levels. For example, in Class Two, you could ask: 'What is halfway between 3 and 9?' In Class Five: 'What is halfway between 423 and 428?'

Counting backwards
This is very helpful in the early classes. But even for Class Four or Five students it can be helpful to ask them to state the five numbers coming before a particularly large number (e.g. 3780).

Remembering large numbers
This is especially good for Class Four and up. Take a problem that everyone could easily do on paper, and have them do it in their head. This requires great concentration and memory.
Examples: 78 + 28; 234 + 38; 612 − 67.

---

* By 'mental arithmetic', we mean doing calculations in your head without writing down your work.

A Teacher's Source Book for Mathematics in Classes 1 to 5

Subtracting from 100, 1000, etc.
This is good practice starting in Class Three.

Examples: 100 – 35; 100 – 72; 600 – 32; 1000 – 222; 500 – 374; 1,000,000 – 36.

Mental arithmetic 'shortcuts'
In our *Student Workbooks in Class Six* and *Class Seven,* there are 27 calculation shortcuts (referred to as 'maths tricks'). Some of the simple ones can be done in Classes Four and Five.

Examples: 300 × 5, 30 × 50, and 4.82 × 10. It is important, however, that there is a process through which the class is guided that brings the students to an understanding of why the trick works (see *Be aware of tricks!* under *The art of teaching maths,* p. 33.)

A word of caution. As with word problems, there is a tendency for some students to give up with mental arithmetic. So the same rules apply: keep it simple, and make it fun! However, it can be best to challenge the students with a tough problem at the end.

Developing a sense of number
Having the students develop a sense of number is an important goal for lower school maths. However, this is very challenging.

It seems that some students were born with a natural sense of number. And for other students it seems as if they will never develop this sense or be able to think mathematically. Yet, often, if we allow the curriculum to soak in, and allow the student to slowly move along with their maths work – all the while being patient and not anxious – then one day (maybe in Class Four or Five) we are pleasantly surprised to see that this student has indeed been able to develop a modest sense of number and a healthy relationship to maths.

Certainly, some of what we do with our maths lessons (for instance, mental arithmetic) directly helps develop the children's sense of number. Yet, just as importantly, and less well understood, is what should be avoided. What follows is an incomplete list of things that can help develop this sense:

Do daily mental arithmetic
Beginning in Class Two, this may be the best way to directly improve the students' sense of number (see also *Mental arithmetic* opposite).

Number dictations
Learning to read and write numbers up into the millions.

Estimating
Starting in Class One with estimating the number of apples in a basket, or the number of people in a room, continuing with larger estimates in Class Two, estimating measurement starting in Class Three, and estimating the answers to difficult vertical arithmetic problems. Estimating is a great way to strengthen the students' sense of number. There are endless possibilities for bringing estimating into the classroom!

Don't force the memorisation of arithmetic facts too early. Often parents and teachers become nervous when they see children using their fingers to do calculations. The real question here is: at what age is counting on your fingers acceptable, and when should a student no longer be doing this? We feel that in Class Two or Three (and perhaps even into Class Four for some students) using fingers to calculate can be positive; this can mean that the child is thinking through the problem, which in general is good for developing a sense of number. If children were to memorise their arithmetic facts in Class Two , then they would miss out on the benefits of 'figuring it out yourself' (for instance, instead of memorising 8 + 5 = 13, they think, 'from 8, I go up by 2 to get to 10, then another 3 to get to 13'). That can do wonders for developing a sense of number!

Allow for different methods
By showing different methods to do calculations, students learn to be flexible and creative in their thinking, which can then help to develop a sense of number. Of course, there needs to be balance. If we always show just one method to solve a problem, then the students can become inflexible in their thinking. At the other extreme, showing different methods to solve almost every problem can confuse and overwhelm many students (see also *Developing flexibility in thinking,* p. 34).

Keep in the horizontal as much as possible
We believe that this is very important. Far too often, students are trained at too young an age to write all arithmetic problems in vertical form. Therefore, 73 − 65, and 65 + 18 are both written vertically. Instead of thinking about the two given numbers and trying to figure out what the answer is – which, of course, helps to develop a sense of number – the problem just becomes a carrying or a borrowing problem, and the student is instead just working with columns of numbers.

Therefore, we recommend that carrying and borrowing not be introduced until Class Three. Even after carrying and borrowing have been introduced, it is important to have the students continue doing arithmetic both in the horizontal form (with practice sheets) and orally with mental arithmetic.

Minimise blind procedures
Related to what has just been said above, in general, procedures where the children follow steps blindly inhibit the development of a sense of number. This does not mean that such procedures (e.g. borrowing, long division, arithmetic with fractions, etc.) should not be done at all. But it may be a reason to delay the introduction of such procedures, and even after a procedure has been introduced, we should be careful to not over-emphasise it. We need to be sure that the students still maintain their ability to do calculations the 'old way' (horizontal arithmetic and mental arithmetic). (See also *Making maths procedural,* p. 10.)

When in doubt, wait! In general, when the students are introduced to a topic before they are developmentally ready, then they will tend to simply follow the procedure without really understanding what they are doing. We should not be asking, 'How soon can I get the children to learn this topic?' but rather, 'Are the children developmentally ready to receive this topic?'

Allow for discovery

There are many times when it is completely appropriate for the teacher to show the class how to do something in maths and then have the children practise it. However, it is important to look for opportunities for the students to discover things on their own. By discovering things on their own, students become excited about learning and the material becomes more meaningful. It also helps to develop flexibility in their thinking. Examples include:

- With addition and multiplication (around Class Two), knowing that the terms can be reversed and the result will be the same (so 6×10 is the same as 10×6).
- When multiplying with zeros (around Class Four), knowing that zeros can be ignored and then added back later (e.g. 40×70, 400×7, and 4×700 are all equal to 2800).
- When subtracting two large numbers (starting around Class Two), we can add instead of subtract to get the answer (e.g. with $73 - 68$, we can think of it as taking 2 steps from 68 to 70, and then 3 steps from 70 up to 73. Our answer is then $2 + 3$, which equals 5).
- When dealing with cost problems (around Class Five), we can first determine the unit cost of one item and then use this to determine the price of a certain number of that item (e.g. if oranges are being sold at a rate of 5 for £1.50, then we first calculate that the unit cost is 30p per orange, so 8 oranges would cost 30×8, which is £2.40).

The art of teaching maths

The three myths of maths

Myth 1

Only people born with maths ability can become good at maths. In reality, hard work can help develop maths ability. In such cases, a student in the upper classes who is seen as being strong in maths, might very well have once struggled. On the other hand, it can happen that a student who had strong ability and never worked at it, ends up quite weak at maths.

Myth 2

Confusion is bad. In reality, confusion is part of learning maths. Every time we learn a new topic in maths, we must go through a period of confusion as we gain clarity. A key difference between a student who is strong at maths versus a student who struggles is that the strong student is usually completely comfortable with working through this period of confusion as they come to clarity, whereas the struggling student often gets frustrated and shuts down (see also *Working with struggling students,* p. 36).

Myth 3

Forgetting is bad. In reality, forgetting is an important part of learning. As teachers, we can sometimes think (perhaps subconsciously) that if we have taught something well, then the students will learn it and won't ever forget it. In Waldorf education, we believe it is important to work with the students' sleep life. It is good and normal for the students to forget something that they have been taught. And if it is something that we want the students to learn permanently, then we need to review it. In fact, for important topics, it can be said in order to learn it permanently, you need to forget it three times!

What does it take to be a good maths teacher?

Many class teachers feel under-confident in their own maths skills, and, in some cases, have had traumatic experiences with maths when they were in school. Often, this results in the teacher developing an antipathy towards maths. However, if a teacher has had bad experiences with maths in their own schooling, it can work to their advantage when teaching. That teacher may be motivated to 'do it differently' and ultimately be determined to find a way to ensure that the class won't have the same negative experiences. Additionally, if such a teacher can find a way to rise above this antipathy, then they may find a newfound joy in maths, which can result in bringing lessons to the children with wonderful enthusiasm.

Still, we should answer the question, 'What makes a good maths teacher?' We believe that the following list includes the most critical elements:

- The teacher needs to be enthusiastic about learning maths. For many teachers, this amounts to finding a new relationship to maths. How wonderful it can be to find out that maths can be interesting and rewarding!
- The teacher needs to be able to present the material effectively. This is the art of teaching.
- The teacher needs adequate time to prepare for the maths lessons. For many teachers, this is the most difficult issue. With everything that is demanded of the class teacher, there often isn't enough time left to prepare adequately for the lessons.
- The teacher must have a healthy relationship to the students. This helps create a safe and comfortable learning environment.

Of course, it should be noted that the above list could really apply to any subject; maths is really no different in this regard.

Communication with parents

The character, commitment, and attitudes of any parent group can vary widely from school to school, and even from class to class. The interests and concerns of a pioneering school are very different from that of a well-established one. For any school, clear communication is critically important. However, given that Waldorf schools tend to attract fairly critical parents, communication needs to be even better than elsewhere. Yet, it often isn't. Many problems at Waldorf schools have been exacerbated by poor communication.

Parents need to be informed of what we are doing and why we are doing it. Beyond simple information exchange, there need to be clear lines of communication to allow parents to express concerns and to allow for discussion and conflict resolution. All of this may seem obvious, but is easier said than done.

In terms of our role as a class teacher, we need to keep parents informed about what is going on in our classroom. This is particularly important when we are doing something out of the ordinary – different than what the parents might expect. For example, in Class Two, it would be best to inform the parents why we want to keep the children in horizontal form with addition and subtraction and why we don't introduce carrying and borrowing until Class Three.

Teaching the 'big topics'

Given that our key focus in Classes One to Four is first to develop a sense of number, and secondly, to have the students learn their arithmetic facts by heart, much of what is said here regarding the 'big topics' (like fractions, percents, algebra, etc.) is more of a concern in Class Five and up. In short, there are two common mistakes made with teaching the 'big topics'.

Too much too soon

Often it is said that 'Class Four is fractions'; 'Class Five is decimals,' etc. Teachers are then misled into thinking that this one topic should be the central theme and dominate the maths lessons for the year. Take the example of fractions in Class Four. Yes, it is important to introduce fractions in Class Four. Many teachers do this well. But too often, much of the rest of Class Four consists of going deeper and deeper into fractions, and then, after a while, much of the class drowns. It may not be recognisable that so many are drowning because on the surface they are 'doing' many fraction problems and getting the right answers.

For example, they may have been taught a method whereby they can follow the procedure for doing a problem like $7\frac{1}{4} - 2\frac{2}{3}$, but often they get 'lost' in the process (even if they do all the correct steps and get the right answer) because they lose sight of what the problem actually was. The real goal with Class Four fractions should only be to have the students develop an enthusiasm for fractions and to have them really understand the fundamental concepts of fractions. The trickier aspects can be covered in the coming years.

Not enough follow-up and review

Often Waldorf teachers do an excellent job introducing a topic in a very thoughtful and creative way, but then it is dropped – forever. Measurement is a classic example. The class is taught a wonderful main lesson on measurement in Class Three and then it isn't touched upon again until middle school. Instead, it should be reviewed and deepened (perhaps only briefly) every year. If we want the students to learn something permanently, then we need to create a 'dance' between introducing, deepening, practising, sleeping, and reviewing.

Timing the introduction to a new topic

All too often, if a teacher is asked, 'Why are you teaching this topic to your students now?' the response is, 'Because that's what everyone does!' An example is borrowing. Most teachers introduce borrowing (and have the children practise it a great deal) in Class Two. Why? 'Because that's when everyone does it.' We should instead ask, 'When is the best time to introduce borrowing?'

If a topic is introduced too early, or studied too deeply and too soon, then two things are likely to happen: many students in the class will get left behind, and even the ones that can keep up will end up simply doing things mechanically without understanding what they are doing. They are then simply following blind procedures instead of developing strategies, developing mental arithmetic skills, and developing flexibility in thinking.

The other extreme – introducing a topic too late – is also problematic. It is best to take the middle road and look for the developmentally appropriate time to bring the topic to the students. Then they will learn the material more deeply, in less time, and with wonderful enthusiasm.

Generally, we should ask the question, 'Why do we do what we do, and when should we do it?' As teachers we need to be able to articulate our answer to this important question to ourselves, to our colleagues, and to our parents. Our answers need to be soundly based upon the pedagogical principles of Waldorf education, and upon the developmental stage and needs of the children.

Regarding main lesson

The main lesson is a central aspect of Waldorf education. In general, the following are some of the key ideas to keep in mind when creating a main lesson for the day:

The rhythm of daily activities may be something like this (note that the times may vary):

Greeting the children. This is a time for shaking the children's hands and having a (perhaps quick) check-in with each individual child before the day begins (time: 10 minutes).

Warm-up. This can include morning verse, songs, poems/recitation, rhythmical exercises, and other exercises related to the subject of the main lesson. The entire warm-up part of the day's main lesson need only take about 25 minutes in Class One and less time in older classes.

Daily review. The review component of the daily main lesson should enkindle enthusiasm for what they heard the previous day. We will then build something new on top of this review (10 minutes).

New material. Every day the students should experience at least a little something new (15 minutes).

Practice. During any maths main lesson, we should include daily practice of the material from the current block, previous blocks, and previous classes (30 minutes or more in Classes Four and Five, less in earlier classes)

Main lesson bookwork. The children should work with material from the previous day(s) and create beautiful work of which they can be proud (20 minutes).

Story. This is simply the story material for the specific class (fables and legends in Class Two, Old Testament in Class Three, Norse mythology in Class Four, and Greek mythology in Class Five). (15–20 minutes).

Flexibility and balance

The amount of time that we spend on each main lesson activity (e.g. warm-up, review and practice, bookwork, etc.) may vary from day to day. Maybe the students need to do certain parts of a movement exercise a few more times, or sing a particular song again, or perhaps they need more practical work. When we see the class becoming sleepy, restless, or not engaged, we have to adjust. If they look pale, then it may be because there has been too much intellectual or memory work going on. If they have very red cheeks, then it may be because there has been too much imagination, drawing, etc. Instead, we try to strike a balance – we like to see rosy cheeks!

Breathing and movement

It is very important to have a healthy in-breathing and out-breathing rhythm every day during main lesson. The teacher should use the main lesson material to keep the children moving throughout the morning.

It may not be best to put all of the movement at the beginning of the main lesson. It is often best to 'read' the students and look for the moments in the lesson when they need some movement.

Starting a new main lesson block

On the first day of a main lesson, we shouldn't start a block with a review of old material from previous blocks. Instead, we should start with something completely new which catches the enthusiasm and curiosity of the students about the new topic. Review of old material should be appropriately woven into the lessons in the following days.

Main lesson books

Main lesson books are the student's own creation. In Waldorf schools, we don't give out a textbook; students create their own book. The main lesson book is every student's self-made textbook!

Progression. A main lesson book should reflect the progress of the lessons over the course of the four weeks. The new concepts should be clearly written down. A parent should be able to follow the line of thought that the teacher has led the class through.

No practice problems should be written in the main lesson book! The students should have a separate practice book. The work in the practice book should also be quite neat.

Pride. It is very important that the students (in all classes!) take pride in their main lesson books.

Beauty. The books should be done beautifully. It is important to teach the students, starting in Class One, how to create a beautiful book. This includes borders, layout, titles, use of colour, etc. While this artistic component is important, remember that the content is even more so.

Completion. There is a tendency in some classes for students not to complete their books and for teachers to even leave a main lesson unfinished. This is very unfortunate! It is very important for students to complete their work. This builds good habits for years into the future. The teacher should frequently check the students' books, so the students get feedback during the block.

Corrections. Starting from Class One, it is important that the teacher reads each student's book and ensures that the student corrects any mistakes.

Reference. Starting in Class Four, the students should be able to use their main lesson books as a reference.

Stories and pictures

The way in which a topic is introduced is very important; this is the strength of many Waldorf teachers. With a mathematics lesson, however, the teacher needs to keep in mind that the stories, pictures, and images that we create for the child are likely to be associated with this topic for a long while. For this reason, a story used to introduce a maths topic ought to be shorter and less elaborate than most other stories. Most importantly, the story should help the students understand the essence of the concept being taught. Then, at the right time, the story should fade away, allowing for the mathematical concept to be discussed and practiced in its pure form without the framework of the story.

This is because we don't want the children to become too dependent upon the story; they need to understand the essence of the concept. It should also be kept in mind that not all maths topics need to be introduced with a story. Telling a story about gnomes collecting a large number of gems and needing to develop a method of counting may be quite helpful for introducing place value to Class Two children, but it may not be helpful to have an elaborate story to introduce long division – it may actually make long division harder for the children to learn.

Additionally, we should be conscious of our use of a visual picture when introducing a maths concept. As teachers, we must be careful to ensure that topics of pure number such as arithmetic, fractions, percents, etc., are developed in the child's mind as free as possible from physical pictures. This doesn't mean that such pictures can never be used. Fractions are more than just pizza, but later we can point out that dividing a pizza is one way to see a fraction. Using manipulatives to help learn addition can be very helpful, but the students also need to see addition done in many ways, never becoming overly reliant on any one physical representation.

If the teacher is cognizant of all of this, it can help the students to better reach the pure concept behind the particular mathematical topic.

Regarding number lines and manipulatives

The number line may be introduced at the end of Class One and then periodically through Class Two as one of several different manipulatives. (Manipulatives are objects designed so that a student can perceive some mathematical concept by manipulating it.) Number lines, like any manipulative, should not be overused, otherwise children could rely on that one manipulative too much, which could inhibit them from getting to the pure number concept. Instead, by seeing things in many different ways, they can then come to understand the pure concept more deeply, and, in the process, become more flexible with their thinking.

It is perhaps best for the number line to be phased out at some point in Class Two. We recommend that the number line not be used to introduce negative numbers in Class Seven. In fact, after Class Two, it could be just fine for the student to not see a number line again until the introduction to Cartesian geometry (i.e. graphing equations) in the upper school.

In general, manipulatives should be used rarely after Class Two for the purpose of learning number concepts and basic arithmetic. Of course, manipulatives do serve quite a useful purpose with more 'physical' maths subjects like measurement and many topics in geometry.

Daily maths practice

In Classes One to Five, maths lessons consist of an interweaving of review, rhythmical exercises, daily practice and bookwork. We recommend doing maths practice every school day throughout the year. As a general guideline, this maths practice should take about 20 to 30 minutes per day during a maths block and 10 minutes per day during other blocks. The material for daily maths practice comes from the current block (when the class is in a maths block), previous blocks, and previous classes.

Be aware of tricks!

Too often, students are taught blind tricks as a means for solving a maths problem while having no idea why or how the trick works. We believe that such blind tricks should generally be avoided. However, the same trick could be taught in a better way such that the students understand it – or, better yet, the trick may be a shortcut that the students discover for themselves. This should be our goal; a strategic trick instead of a blind trick. Even if the discovery of the trick is led by a few of the 'quicker' students in the class, it is valuable for the whole class to see that it comes from a process.

For example, consider this problem: Convert $4\frac{3}{5}$ into an improper fraction. If the students are just told that you need to multiply 4 times 5 and then add 3, then it becomes a blind trick because they don't have an understanding of what they are doing. However, if they have been led through the process with the teacher, and the class as a whole has come to an understanding of why it works, then this trick has become part of a strategy.

Other tricks include borrowing, dividing with fractions (when you invert the second fraction and multiply), and cross-cancelling when multiplying fractions.

Again, it's not that these tricks can't be done with the children. The point here is that rather than having the teacher introduce a trick by telling children what the trick is, the children should feel that they played a part in the discovery of it. This makes all the difference between a 'blind trick' and a 'strategic trick'.

Developing flexibility in thinking

Unfortunately, many students have the impression that for any given maths problem there is only one correct answer and one way to derive it. Maths is then seen as a rigid and unimaginative subject. We must then look for opportunities to counter this impression. This is one aspect of the wisdom of working from the whole to the part. During a Class One maths lesson, if we ask, 'What is 12?' we can think of all possible correct answers: 4×3, 6×2, $9 + 3$, $15 - 3$, etc. Then in Class Two, it can be fascinating to ask the students how they can calculate $23 - 15$. In Class Four, the teacher can show different ways to do long division – perhaps there is a parent from another country who can demonstrate how they were taught to do long division. In these ways, the students can then see that maths is flexible, creative and imaginative. This also makes maths more interesting for the students, helps to develop flexibility in their thinking and, in turn, furthers their sense of number.

Avoiding the 'great divide'

We can feel pressured to have our maths class move more quickly and show that 'my class is indeed doing advanced maths'. By doing this, we might impress a few parents and colleagues, and it may make some of the quicker students happy, but we are much more likely then to overwhelm some and increase the disparity between the stronger and weaker students. This may also lead to more students relying upon blind procedures rather than understanding the concepts. (See *Maths trauma*, p. 12)

By Class Four, the level between the students usually begins to widen. Hopefully, every student is comfortable at their own level. We need to be careful that we don't increase this 'divide'. All too often, classes enter middle school with a great divide between those who are good at maths and those who are traumatised by maths. Usually, this extreme situation can be avoided. The key to avoiding the great divide is to make sure the 'slower' students aren't getting lost and overwhelmed.

But then the question that can be asked is: 'What about the quicker students? Won't they be bored?' A few things can be said about this. First of all, in the lower classes, when a student says: 'maths is easy', it usually isn't really a complaint. That student is usually quite pleased with understanding the material so well. And often, when a student in Class Two or Three is complaining about being bored, there may be something else going on. It could have something to do with being exposed to media at home – too much fast and short visual impressions through TV or computers can make it difficult for students to think and concentrate at school. Some students are so used to being entertained all day that they cannot entertain themselves, making school seem boring in comparison.

However, the quicker students also need challenges (especially after Class Three); it is important to keep these students engaged. The students shouldn't always be doing the exact same thing. At times, we should give different problems to students of different levels so that the 'slower' students don't get overwhelmed and the quicker students are adequately challenged. For example, with a practice sheet that has vertical arithmetic problems like 73 + 45, we could add a few challenge problems, like 5736 + 2658, at the end. Or, from time to time, the quicker student can help out a fellow classmate. Or maybe a student needing 'something extra' can even make up a maths sheet for the next day.

This is all part of the art of teaching: How can we reach our goals without losing the students that tend to struggle?

Be careful of using maths in a competitive way!

While games and competition can be fun for many of the students, they can leave a few students feeling bad. For this reason, we encourage teachers to be very discerning about what games they bring into the classroom. Simply ask yourself, 'Could this game make some-one feel bad?' We especially discourage games where students are required to stand up in front of the class (e.g. maths-around-the-world, or maths-baseball) and compete against one another. For some students, to lose in front of everyone in this way can be quite humiliating. On the other hand, a simple maths board game played between friends could be fun and instructive.

In a similar way, we discourage posting in the classroom a list with names of the students who have mastered certain times tables. Imagine how the last one feels!

Additionally, before Class Five, it is good to find ways to keep it a secret as to who is taking the longest to complete their maths practice sheets. One way to do this is to instruct the students to immediately begin another task (e.g. reading a book) quietly at their desk so that it isn't obvious who the slowest students are. It can also be fine to allow only a certain period of time to work on a practice sheet or a set of problems – when the time is up, then the students stop working. It's fine if some students get further along than others.

Regarding testing

In mainstream education, standardised testing has become more important than ever. Indeed, it drives much of what is done in the classroom. We believe that such testing is detrimental to the children and to the learning process. The major purpose of 'testing' should be that the teacher is informed of the students' progress. In this sense, we should be 'testing' every day (e.g. through oral exercises and practice sheets – and keep our own records of the students' progress), but the students (even into middle school) should never be conscious of any testing. Beginning in the early classes we should create an attitude in the students such that they naturally want to do their best – to show their teacher, and themselves, how much they have learned.

What to do when things aren't going well

Relax. Parents are often fearful. This gets through to the students and pressures the teacher, who in turn becomes fearful and anxious. Try not to have your teaching driven by anxiety and fear.

Parent communication. Speak to parents in parent evenings and individually. Parents need to understand clearly what you are doing and why, especially if it is different than the norm. Parents need to be well informed. They need to know what their child has achieved and what their child needs to work on.

Ask yourself, 'Why am I doing this?' The answer shouldn't be, 'because that's how everyone does it.' We should have a real pedagogical answer that we can give to ourselves, our parents, and our colleagues.

Give it a rest. Re-evaluate what you're doing. Doing more isn't necessarily helpful. Maybe if a particular topic is put to rest for a month or two – or even until next year – then the class will really absorb it better at that later time.

Make sure that the timing is right. When should we introduce a certain topic? The question shouldn't be, 'How soon can I do it?' but rather, 'Is this the developmentally appropriate time to introduce this topic?' If it seems that many of the students aren't ready for something, then it may be wise to listen to that instinct. When in doubt, wait!

Remember your role. Remember that one of our important roles is as 'maths coach' – to help these children through their emotional maths issues.

Working with struggling students

Four steps towards maths trauma

Confusion. Everyone experiences confusion when learning maths. We can think of confusion as the state you are in as you are working towards clarity. Therefore, confusion is necessary as you are learning something new. Students who are deemed to be 'good at maths' are usually comfortable with being confused, while for others, being confused can bring up many emotions, which may inhibit learning.

Struggling. Most students struggle with maths at least occasionally. Normally, when learning a new maths topic, the period of confusion should be fairly short. If not, then students may struggle for a period of time until clarity is achieved. In general, one of our goals (especially in the middle and upper school) is for all of the students to experience struggle and learn how to work through it.

Frustration. Many students get frustrated with maths. Typically, students become frustrated after struggling for an extended period of time. Some students get to a level of frustration almost as soon as they get confused. For many of these students, we need to help them learn to cope with their frustration without taking it personally ourselves.

Shutting down/trauma. Some students shut down and become maths traumatised. After a while, if students are constantly frustrated with maths and don't ever quite understand the concepts, then they start to believe that it's impossible and give up.

One of the jobs of a class teacher is to guide the students through the challenges they encounter in school and in life. In today's world, our children are often shielded from discomfort; they come to expect that things should be easy. They have little patience. It is therefore not surprising that so many children have little tolerance for confusion and struggle. If we compound this with a variety of emotional issues, then we can see how important it is for us, as teachers, to coach these students through these challenges.

Perfectionism and fear of failure

Some students have a tendency towards perfectionism. Often it is a girl who wants everything to be in order. Often, it is one of the stronger students in the class. Perfectionists want life to be rhythmical and predictable. And in terms of schoolwork, they want to do well in everything. When faced with a task, they need to be confident that they can do it.

The core of the difficulty is that maths often violates these rules. Confusion and learning to overcome your struggles is part of doing maths. To some degree, especially in middle school and above, maths is about facing the unknown and figuring out how to solve unfamiliar problems. To a perfectionist, all of this is threatening.

And then the student enters adolescence, becomes more self-aware, and maths becomes even more unpleasant and scary. Such a student may eventually just give up on maths. Why? Because it is less painful to give up than it is to put forth effort and, in the end, perhaps fail anyway. This is known as 'fear of failure'.

So what can we do as teachers? Once again, our role as a coach is critical. And this is bigger than just maths. We need to look for situations where they feel they can't succeed, but we know they can. Such a situation could be having a role in a class play, climbing a mountain, riding a bicycle (or a unicycle!), or solving a particularly daunting maths problem. They think they can't, and we know they can. At the right time, and in the right way, we need to gently push them into these situations. Our role is to coach them through their challenges, and to help ensure their success. And once they succeed, celebrate! 'Look at what you did! And you thought you couldn't do it!' After that, we can build on this success. In this way, the student's confidence is slowly increased, and, over time, the student becomes more comfortable with the challenges that life presents, and hopefully becomes more open to learning maths.

Support for learning

Meeting the needs of a child with learning challenges can take a good deal of time and energy.* In most cases, the problems are in the realm of the lower senses – be it a problem with balance, sense of life and/or gross-motor movement. Often, these children cannot even count one step while saying 'one'. This makes it more difficult for them to develop a sense of number.

In general, we can always expect to have students who are somewhat behind the rest of the class. In this case, it is especially important for the teacher to know where the child is at, to understand why there is an issue, and to have a plan of how to move forward.

Confidence is an important factor. We need to figure out where the child gets stuck and pick it up from there, so the child starts to build confidence. The students need to know that their teacher believes in them. Children shouldn't feel that they are doing 'dumbed-down maths'. If a child (or the class as a whole) is behind or has certain holes in their knowledge, then we still have to find ways to bring the current material to them.

Dealing with all of this shouldn't just fall on the shoulders of the class teacher. There are often additional hindrances that obstruct the learning of maths. As teaching staff, we can work together (for instance, with child study) to figure out what is behind this.

Individual coaching often makes a huge difference. The class teacher should ask the remedial teacher for help early on; waiting until Class Five is too late. Any emotional damage takes significant time to heal and can further delay the child's progress with maths. Some children with remedial needs (especially if we are able to work with the situation effectively) can be behind the rest of the class for years, but then they can 'wake up' to maths in a later class – maybe in Class Five, or even as late as Class Eight.

Additionally, we need to be careful not to allow fear to set in with ourselves, the student, or the parents – fear exacerbates the situation. We need to work productively with the parents of a child with remedial needs. Clear communication with parents is critical. This includes having a written record (as a school document) of the child's progress and of any modifications in the child's programme (an individual learning plan).

Depending upon a school's resources, it may not be feasible to keep a child with serious learning challenges in the school. Sometimes, in spite of our own emotional attachments to the child, we have to admit that we can't meet a child's needs.

---

* For more ideas on working with children with learning challenges, see Ernst Schuberth's book, *Teaching Mathematics for First and Second Grades in Waldorf Schools*, pp. 59ff.

A Teacher's Source Book for Mathematics in Classes 1 to 5

Golden rules

Healthy maths

Choose developmentally appropriate material. Is the material meeting the children? How does this topic affect the children developmentally?

When in doubt, wait. Would the children be more able to receive this if you waited until later?

Less is more! Are you overdoing a new topic? Are you simply 'plowing through' the material?

Minimise blind procedures and tricks. Are the students blindly following procedures and doing tricks without understanding? If so, could this be done differently?

Healthy students

Enthusiastic students. Are the students interested and enthused?

Challenging the students. Are you challenging the students appropriately?

Avoiding trauma. Are they getting it? Is it too much for some? Are some students' confidence and enthusiasm being damaged? Is the learning environment healthy, so that students can learn?

Healthy teacher

Enthusiastic teacher. Are you interested and enthused?

Health and balance. Are you healthy and balanced with a strong inner life?

Relationship to the material. Are you the author of what you bring to the class? Are you clear about why you are teaching this topic now to these students? Do you see the 'big picture'?

Relationship with the children. The material is not the most important thing. What matters is how you bring it, who you are in front of the children, and your relationship with them.

Class One Maths

Overview of child development in Class One

With the change of teeth, the capacity of thinking is revealed, and the desire to learn and to follow a beloved authority becomes apparent. Instead of imitating the surrounding world at will, the children focus more on following their teacher. Thus, the first school year is still marked by a 'dreaming living' in the world. This is a ripple effect from the early childhood years. There is an eagerness for learning and the children want to engage through their feelings. They connect with the subject matter through rhymes, music, movement, etc. Through images, the spoken word enlivens the children's thinking. As their teacher, we want them to work willingly, and we use images to motivate them. Instead of saying, 'Write your numbers straight,' we say, 'Let all your numbers stand as straight as a spear.' Of course, all the work should be presented with joy and enthusiasm.

For teaching maths in Class One, this means we use stories (a baker who makes muffins and puts them into rows of two, or on plates in groups of four, or he sells them in groups of three). The students illustrate these stories in their main lesson books. The teacher can vary things every day while working with the same concept and story.

Curriculum summary for Class One maths

The world of numbers

Roman numerals. We begin with the Roman numerals because they are related to the human body. The (standard) Arabic numbers can be introduced afterwards.

Quality of numbers. What is the quality of numbers that we see in the world?

Counting. Practise counting forwards and backwards to 100. The children need to become 'at ease'* with this.

Number dictations. Number dictations should start in the second maths block.

Developing a sense of number

The sense for numbers is awakening. The goal in Class One is for the children to come to conscious counting through movement. Else Göttgens calls this 'counting along the line'.†

Whole to the part. As mentioned in the introduction, working from the whole to the part is an important aspect of our work. This is especially true in Class One. For example, instead

---

* Throughout this book, we use the following terms: *fluent* means they need to have it on the tip of their tongues without any hesitation. *At/with ease* means they need to feel comfortable but there might still be some hesitation. Therefore, we have three stages in learning a skill: introduction, at ease, and fluent.

† Else Göttgens, *Waldorf Education in Practice*, p. 35.

of always asking questions like, 'What is 9 + 3?' we can instead ask, 'What is 12?' Think of the possibilities!

The children should gradually come to see a number as an entity in itself. This is important. Can they immediately recognise a group of five on a dice, a flash of three fingers, or a group of six nuts? The children can make their own flashcards from these examples.

Rhythmical counting serves as preparation for learning the times tables in Class Two. In Class One, the children learn to do rhythmical counting by 2s, 3s, 4s, 5s, 10s, and 11s. This work should come out of the imagination. In Class One, we should always count by ones, but emphasise the given number. For example, with rhythmical counting by 3s, we count forwards and backwards while emphasising every third number, perhaps by clapping and saying it louder: 1, 2, **3**, 4, 5, **6**, 7, 8, **9**, 10, 11, **12,** etc. We don't need to mention that this is the 3 times table; we simply call it rhythmical counting by 3s. No rhythmical counting is done in Class One between the maths main lessons – it goes to sleep during those time periods.

Movement. Maths is related to the physical body. In order to become aware of mathematical processes, children need to move their body. For many children in Class One, it is a challenge to synchronise their movement with their voice. Their voice is usually faster than the movement of either their hands or their feet.

Estimating. We can ask: 'How many steps am I from the board?' or 'How many giant steps am I from the door?' In this way, the child tries to find his position in the world, which helps to develop a spatial orientation.

Beginning calculations

Regrouping numbers. For example, how can we regroup the number ten? There are many answers: 2 groups of five, five groups of two, 6 and 4, 7 and 3, etc.

Introducing the four processes. The students should be fluent with sums (e.g. 8 + 5) up to 24, and with ease up to 100.

Learning the 'easy' addition facts. All addition facts up to 10, as well as all of the doubles (i.e. 6 + 6, 7 + 7, 8 + 8, 9 + 9) should be learned by heart by the end of Class One.

Recommended reading

Henning Anderson, *Active Arithmetic.*

Herman von Baravalle, *The Teaching of Arithmetic and the Waldorf School Plan.*

Irene Groh, Mona Ruef, *Education and Teaching as Preventive Medicine,* pp. 117–31.

Dorothy Harrer, *Math Lessons For Elementary Grades.*

Ernst Schuberth, *Teaching Mathematics for First and Second Grades in Waldorf Schools.*

Rudolf Steiner, *The Spiritual Ground of Education,* lecture 5.

Rudolf Steiner, *The Kingdom of Childhood,* lecture 5.

Publication details of the above titles are under *Suggested Reading,* p. 125.

Lessons and topics for Class One maths

It is especially important not to go on working in a monotonous way, doing nothing but adding for six months, etc., but where possible one should take all four arithmetic rules fairly quickly one after another and then practise them…We should take all four rules at once and be careful that through practise these four rules are mastered almost at the same time. (Rudolf Steiner)

Background reading. Be sure to reread the chapter, *Teaching Maths in Lower Classes*, p. 9.

Mental arithmetic. Mental arithmetic is integrated into the maths lessons through the use of imaginative number stories.

Scheduling. The curriculum calls for 12 weeks of maths in Class One, usually one main lesson block at the end of October, one in January, and one in March. A one-week review of maths can be done at the year's end.

Maths main lesson block 1

Content overview

Quality of the numbers 1–12, with Roman and Arabic numerals. Find an image for every number, perhaps using an ongoing story where the central question is: Where is there only one of something in the world? Where is there two? Where is there three, etc?

Counting. Practise counting up to 24 (forwards and backwards) with ease, and up to 100 with joy!

Rhythmical counting. During this first block, we can do rhythmical counting by 2s and 4s. We should practise going both forwards and backwards.

Regrouping. The idea of regrouping is briefly introduced here. It quite naturally comes out of our work with going from the whole to the part (for instance, 'How can we regroup the number ten?' There are many answers: 2 groups of five, five groups of two, 6 and 4, 7 and 3, etc.)

Writing. Practise writing the numbers 1 to 12. Always start at the top of the digit's written form, and draw towards the bottom.

The four processes ($+, -, \times, \div$) are briefly introduced, but only orally. (In the second maths block the students write them down for the first time.)

Movement

Speaking and moving should go together. This is very important for the development of maths capacities.*

Count from 1 to 24. Practise counting by using one step per number, using images. For example, have the children imagine going over stepping-stones across a river, or dwarfs stepping into a dark cave where they collect gems, jewels, etc. Have them then walk and count backwards as they go back home again.

Here are some examples of *rhythmical counting* (hopping, clapping, stamping, etc.).

- For *counting by twos,* the dwarfs move the axes rhythmically: 1, *2,* 3, *4,* 5, *6,* 7, *8,* 9, *10,* etc.
- *Even and odd numbers.* The farmer who lost one wooden shoe in the heavy clay: Because the farmer (and the children) only have one shoe on, we can only hear one of the steps clearly. It goes like this: 1, *2,* 3, *4,* 5, etc., where we whisper the 1, 3, 5 and speak the other ones loudly. Of course, the children can use boots instead of wooden shoes. On the next day, the farmer might lose the other shoe or boot, so we would count the odd numbers instead.
- *Very important!* After we have finished a movement, the children should stand still and say the sequence of numbers once again, forward and backwards without movement. In this way, we bring the will activity to consciousness.

* Else Göttgens, *Waldorf Education in Practice,* p. 37.

Working with manipulatives

Counting should be connected to an object, starting with their own fingers and toes. Different objects may be: chestnuts, gems, etc. Try to avoid counting with food (beans, lentils, etc.). Unless you are eating it, food is not something to play with in a world where there is hunger.

Regrouping numbers

The children put both of their hands on their desk, and we ask the students to show four fingers in the air with one hand. We can then ask, how many different ways are there to show four fingers if you can use both hands? (One way would be one finger on one hand and three fingers on the other hand.)

The teacher can also hold up four fingers, and the child needs to immediately recognise that there are four fingers. This demands a lot of practice as the children learn to move away from counting. This can also be done by using different objects on a table under a cloth, etc. For example, imagine using a certain amount of chestnuts. We show them very briefly and then cover them up. We then ask the children how many chestnuts they saw. The idea is that we want them to see the amount immediately instead of counting every single nut. This can also be done using flashcards.

The five-structure

This is also the first visual encounter with the five-structure. The five-structure is the five fingers on our hands; two hands make ten. It is easy for most children to work with units of five. This becomes quite useful later when we start to develop strategies. It is perhaps the first strategy they will use.

We should also ask the students to regroup a number of gems. For example, using 12 gems, there are many possibilities: *** *** *** *** or ** ** ** ** ** ** or **** **** **** or ***** ** * ****.

Making geometrical forms with manipulatives
In his book, *Active Arithmetic,* Henning Anderson has the children draw a circle on a piece of paper and then asks them to put three (or another number) chestnuts somewhere on the circle. There are different possibilities, but most students try to find a harmony and will make a perfect equilateral triangle. Rudolf Steiner also spoke about the importance of these activities.*

Review and practice
The importance of review
We must emphasise here, once again, the importance of how the teacher must be conscious of using the child's sleep life as part of the learning process. The teacher must review (that is, bring back into the child's imagination) the new material from the previous day, perhaps by using different materials. We might regroup 12 children, and then the next day, during the review, we might regroup 12 chairs.

Writing numbers
We should practise writing numbers in a sand tray, on paper, using small blackboards, or go outside and practise writing numbers with sticks. Remember to always get the children to write the numbers from top to bottom.

Movement exercises
We should practise movement exercises with counting every day, but each day we use different variations. For example, we can imagine 12 dwarfs going into a cave, while the rest of the students are fireflies watching them. In this way, some students are observing what the others are doing. This brings a different consciousness to the process. Once again, we expect to see that movement while simultaneously speaking can be quite difficult.

Regrouping
After the number 12 has been reviewed, we practise the same regrouping with a different number.

Bookwork
In this block, the children can make drawings in their books from the qualities of the first 12 numbers. They can write the twelve Roman numerals here, and perhaps the Arabic numerals as well.

The children's main lesson book should include a few examples of number regrouping.

Visit *www.JamieYorkPress.com* to see full-colour pages from students' main lesson books.

* Rudolf Steiner, *The Child's Changing Consciousness,* lecture of April 17, 1923.

Maths main lesson block 2

Content overview

The four processes. In the first maths main lesson, the four processes were briefly introduced orally, but they weren't written down. Now, for the first time, the four processes are written down.

Counting. The children should now be able to count with ease up to 100.

Rhythmical counting. During this second block, we should review rhythmical counting by 2s and 4s, and then add the 5s, 10s and 3s. Remember to practise going both forwards and backwards. How far we get with this work depends upon the abilities of the class.

Regrouping. We should continue our work started in the first main lesson with regrouping numbers.

Writing. We continue what we started during the first maths block. Remember to always write the numbers from the top (of the digit's written form) progressing to the bottom. We can now start doing some number dictations up to 24.

New material

Introduction of the four processes

Each process (plus, minus, times, and divide) is introduced through four characters, each having one of the four temperaments.* Addition (plus) is phlegmatic, keeping as much

as possible; subtraction (minus) is melancholic, carelessly losing things; multiplication (times) is sanguine, working as quickly as possible; and division (divide) is choleric, sharing everything fairly.

Of course, the children have already worked with these four processes through regrouping activities and through our maths stories during our first maths block. But now we introduce the signs of the four processes ($+$, $-$, $\times$, $\div$) visually.

Addition and multiplication are introduced from the whole to the parts.

Examples: $8 = 5 + 3$
$14 = 2 \times 7$

Subtraction starts from the difference.

Example: A girl picks flowers in the field. She picks 12 flowers, but she counts only 9 flowers when she gets home. How many flowers did she lose?

Likewise, division starts from the quotient.

Example: 12 rabbits were playing in the field and suddenly the fox appeared. The rabbits ran to their homes, but there were only 3 homes, and every home could only have the same number of rabbits. This is also a social activity.

At the end of the game we bring this problem to consciousness. So we can write:

$12 = 4 + 4 + 4$ or $12 = 3 \times 4$ or $12 \div 3 = 4$ or $12 - 4 - 4 - 4 = 0$ (then there are no rabbits left.)

During this block, we play with these concepts using the four processes.

---

* Ernst Schuberth, *Teaching Mathematics for First and Second Grades in Waldorf Schools*, pp. 34–48, also Dorothy Harrer, *Math Lessons For Elementary Grades*.

Movement

In the first maths main lesson block, we did a counting movement using the image of a farmer with one wooden shoe. Now we can create new stories that call for different activities and counting movements.

We start on a different number (e.g. 12 or 15), and count up from there until 36 or 42. We can also do this backwards. This helps the students to become confident with moving up and down past the tens (i.e. past 20, 30, 40, etc.).

Example: 27, 28, 29, 30, 31, 32, 33, 34, 35, 36, 36, 35, 34, 33, 32, 31, 30, 29, 28, 27.

Rhythmical counting

Practise rhythmical counting with the 2s, 3s, 4s, 5s, 10s and 11s. Slowly, with the 2s, 3s and 4s, the students can say only the numbers in the tables (as opposed to earlier in the year when they were saying every number and emphasising the numbers in the table). With the 5s, 10s, and 11s, the students can immediately jump into counting by 5s, 10s and 11s.

Working with manipulatives

Work with regrouping the numbers 1 to 24, using manipulatives and/or fingers.

Students can work in pairs. For example, with the number 8, the teacher writes all the different possibilities on the board, and the students find as many regroupings as possible, such as: $8 = 2 + 6$, $8 = 1 + 7$, $8 = 7 + 1$, $8 = 4 + 4$. There are, of course, many more possibilities, but some of them cannot be made with our fingers.

The next day, review the regrouping that was done yesterday, and then use the T-form to organise it:

$$
\begin{array}{c|c}
\multicolumn{2}{c}{8} \\
\hline
0 & 8 \\
1 & 7 \\
2 & 6 \\
3 & 5 \quad \text{etc.}
\end{array}
$$

Now we can practise with these regroupings in the following way: Using your right hand, cover the section on the right side of the vertical line (we have to show this to the students) and now we will say: '8 is 1 plus what?' (they need to figure out the 7 and they can check it under their hand). Then they move down and say: '8 is 2 plus what?'

Review and practice

As always, the new material should be reviewed every day.

Continue practising writing numbers, and regularly doing number dictations up to 24.

We should use the T-form to work with regrouping many different numbers.

Bookwork

The main lesson book needs to be artistic – much more than just dry numbers.

Get the children to show the use of the T-form to regroup the numbers 1–24.

They can begin to include some problems in their books that use the signs $(+, -, \times, \div)$ of the four processes, such as $8 = 4 + 4$, $8 = 10 - 2$, $8 = 2 \times 4$, $8 \div 2 = 4$, etc.

Have the children draw pictures from the stories in their maths lessons, which should include the characters of these stories (from the fox and rabbit story, Mini Minus, David Divide, etc.). They should also carefully draw the signs for the four processes (+, −, ×, ÷).

Visit *www.JamieYorkPress.com* to see full-colour pages from students' main lesson books.

Maths main lesson block 3

Content overview

Practising counting. All students should be very fluent counting (forwards and backwards) up to 24, and at ease with counting (forwards and backwards) up to 100.

The four processes. All students are becoming fluent with working with the four processes up to 10, and becoming more at ease with the four processes up to 24.

Strategies. Introduce some strategies. This is a preview of a theme carried into Class Two. In Class One, these strategies come out of our work with regrouping.

Rhythmical counting. This important work continues what was begun in the first two maths blocks. By the end of Class One, it is good for the children to have worked regularly with rhythmical counting with the 2s, 3s, 4s, 5s, 10s and 11s.

New material

Progressing from counting to maths

The children now begin to move beyond counting and learn to think more 'mathematically', as they develop more of a sense of number. In this way, they begin to learn strategies for doing calculations, especially involving addition and subtraction. In order to do this, the teacher should be aware of the step-by-step progression for teaching addition, subtraction, etc. (see p. 49).

Learning the 'easy' addition facts

This requires the use of memory forces. All addition facts up to 10, as well as all of the doubles $(6 + 6, 7 + 7, 8 + 8, 9 + 9)$ should be known by heart by the end of Class One.

Strategies for larger facts

The students should begin to use strategies. For example, with $5 + 6$ we could do $5 + 5 + 1$ or $6 + 6 - 1$. Using $12 - 4$ as another example, they could think of it as $12 - 2 - 2$, or even arrive at the answer by counting by 4s. Since both 4 and 12 are in the 4 times table, the answer, 8, is also in the 4 times table. It is wonderful for the students to share the strategies that they have discovered with the class!

Movement

Previously, the whole class did rhythmical counting exercises together. Now we need to do this in small groups and individually too.

The four steps for movement exercises

The following four steps are quite important. Here is an example using 12 + __ = 19.

Step 1: Have the students stand on 12 on a number line on the floor. How many steps are there to get to 19? In this case they are doing three things: stepping, speaking the numbers (starting with 13), and counting the steps on their fingers. In the end (after reaching 19), we can ask different questions, like: 'What is the difference between 12 and 19?' or '12 plus what is 19?' or 'What is 19 minus 12?'

Step 2: The children stand still and speak out loud the same problem (12 + __ = 19) without moving. They speak the numbers 13, 14, 15, 16, 17, 18, 19 while counting on their fingers each step.

Step 3: The children sit down and write down what just was spoken. Now they write down the problem: 12 + 7 = 19. (The children could also use their small blackboards to practise this.)

Step 4: The children read back what is written down.

Rhythmical counting

Continue practising rhythmical counting with the 2s, 3s, 4s, 5s, 10s and 11s (see *Rhythmical counting* in block 2, p. 46). We can now work with the tables more in depth.

For example, with the twos, we move the row of twos (2, 4, 6, 8, etc.). The whole class moves it (e.g. walking) forwards and backwards. Then the whole class stands still while speaking the row of 2. Then they sit down and from memory write down the row of twos on their little blackboards. Then they read back aloud the row 2, 4, 6, 8, etc.

Working with manipulatives

Fading out manipulatives

At this point in the Class One year, it is important to get away from working with manipulatives. The students can now imagine the problem and then find ways to solve it.

Introducing larger numbers

With the smaller numbers (up to 24), we try to not use manipulatives at this point, but some children may still need some visual help. We could provide them with a string of 20 wooden beads, coloured in the five-structure, as shown with the photo above.

Number line

This can be the right time to bring the number line (up to 100) into the classroom. This should be practised both ways: saying a number that is pointed at, and finding a number that is spoken.

Games

Try to find engaging games using the number line (see Henning Anderson's book), as well as dice and board games (see the Appendix, p. 111 for a list of games for lower school maths). These can be wonderful things for the children to do when there is extra time.

Review and practice
Number dictations
We can now do number dictations up to 100.

The four processes
Continue writing and practising problems that use the four processes.

Patterns with numbers
- The children should visualise problems they did with manipulatives in previous blocks.
- We should continue practising the regrouping of numbers.
- Look for ways to show the pattern of numbers. Baravalle's book has many wonderful ideas for this. Here are a couple of examples (using triangular and square numbers – but we don't need to mention these terms to the children):

$$1 = 1 \rightarrow 1$$
$$1 + 2 = 3 \rightarrow 3 - 1 = 2$$
$$1 + 2 + 3 = 6 \rightarrow 6 - 3 = 3$$
$$1 + 2 + 3 + 4 = 10 \rightarrow 10 - 6 = 4$$
etc.
or
$$1 = 1 \rightarrow 1 \times 1 = 1 \rightarrow 1$$
$$1 + 3 = 4 \rightarrow 2 \times 2 = 4 \rightarrow 4 - 1 = 3$$
$$1 + 3 + 5 = 9 \rightarrow 3 \times 3 = 9 \rightarrow 9 - 4 = 5$$
$$1 + 3 + 5 + 7 = 16 \rightarrow 4 \times 4 = 16 \rightarrow 16 - 9 = 7$$
etc.

Bookwork
Baravalle's book can be a nice guide for the main lesson bookwork.

Work done with the number line can be put into the students' book in a visual way (e.g. showing rabbits hopping on the line from one number to the next, skipping numbers at times, etc.).

The children can write all of the numbers from 1 to 100 in a list into their main lesson books.

The layout and use of colour in the main lesson book is all very important. See full-colour pages from students' main lesson books at *www.JamieYorkPress.com*.

Step-by-step progressions
Addition
Keep in mind that these steps for addition are happening concurrently with a similar step-by-step progression for subtraction (see next page).

This is intended to give the teacher some possible ideas of what could be done to work in a structured way.

There are more steps possible than are listed below.

Step 1: Regrouping 10
Ask: 'What is 10?'
$$10 = 1 + 9$$
$$10 = 2 + 8$$
$$10 = 3 + 7$$
etc.

Step 2: Adding up to 10

$1 + 9 = \underline{}$

$2 + 8 = \underline{}$

$3 + 7 = \underline{}$

etc.

Step 3: Finding the missing number using 10

$10 = 1 + \underline{}$

$10 = 2 + \underline{}$

$10 = \underline{} + 7$

$10 = \underline{} + 9$

etc.

Step 4: Regrouping 20

Ask: 'What is 20?'

$20 = 11 + 9$

$20 = 12 + 8$

$20 = 13 + 7$

etc.

Step 5: Adding up to 20, such as:

$11 + 9 = \underline{}$

$12 + 8 = \underline{}$

$13 + 7 = \underline{}$

etc.

Step 6: Finding the missing number using 20

$20 = 11 + \underline{}$

$20 = \underline{} + 8$

etc.

Step 7: Working with doubles

$2 = \underline{} + \underline{} \rightarrow 1 + 1 = \underline{}$

$4 = \underline{} + \underline{} \rightarrow 2 + 2 = \underline{}$

etc. up to $20 = 10 + 10$

Step 8: Add two 1-digit numbers for a sum between 11 and 18, such as:

$11 = 5 + \underline{} \rightarrow 5 + 6 = \underline{}$

$15 = 7 + \underline{} \rightarrow 7 + 8 = \underline{}$

etc.

Step 9: Add a 2-digit number to a 1-digit number, up to a sum of 20, such as:

$10 + 2 = \underline{} \rightarrow 12 = 10 + \underline{}$

$12 + 4 = \underline{} \rightarrow 16 = 12 + \underline{}$

$8 + 12 = \underline{} \rightarrow 20 = 8 + \underline{}$

etc.

Step 10: Add a 2-digit and a 1-digit number, for a sum between 21 and 24

$15 + 6 = \underline{} \rightarrow 21 = 15 + \underline{}$

$18 + 5 = \underline{} \rightarrow 23 = 18 + \underline{}$

$17 + 7 = \underline{} \rightarrow 24 = 17 + \underline{}$

etc.

Subtraction

Keep in mind that these steps for subtraction are happening concurrently with a similar step-by-step progression for addition.

Here again, there are many more steps and variations possible. We would like to encourage teachers to find more steps.

Step 1: The first steps

$1 = 1 - \underline{} \rightarrow 1 - 0 = \underline{}$

$1 = 2 - \underline{} \rightarrow 2 - \underline{} = 1$

$1 = 3 - \underline{}$ etc.

$2 = 2 - \underline{} \rightarrow 2 - 0 = \underline{}$

$2 = 3 - \underline{} \rightarrow 3 - \underline{} = 2$

$2 = 4 - \underline{}$ etc.

Step 2: Subtracting with 10 and under

$10 = 10 - \_\_ \to 10 - 0 = 1\_\_$
$9 = 10 - \_\_ \to 10 - \_\_ = 9$
$8 = 10 - \_\_$ etc.
$9 = 9 - \_\_ \to 9 - \_\_ = 9$
$8 = 9 - \_\_ \to 9 - 1 = \_\_$
$7 = 9 - \_\_$ etc.
$8 = 8 - \_\_ \to \_\_ - 0 = 8$
$7 = \_\_ - 1 \to 8 - 1 = \_\_$
$6 = 8 - \_\_$ etc.

Step 3: Subtracting numbers 20 and under with a result of 10, or greater

$20 = 20 - \_\_ \to 20 - 0 = \_\_$
$19 = 20 - \_\_ \to 20 - \_\_ = 19$
$18 = 20 - \_\_$ etc.
$19 = 19 - \_\_ \to \_\_ - 0 = 19$
$18 = 19 - \_\_ \to 19 - \_\_ = 18$
$17 = 19 - \_\_$ etc.
$18 = 18 - \_\_ \to 18 - 0 = \_\_$
$17 = 18 - \_\_ \to 18 - \_\_ = 17$
$16 = 18 - \_\_$ etc.

Step 4: Subtracting a 1-digit number from between 11 and 19 with a result less than 10

$9 = 11 - \_\_ \to 11 - 2 = \_\_$
$8 = 11 - \_\_ \to 11 - 3 = \_\_$
$7 = 11 - \_\_$ etc.
$9 = 12 - \_\_ \to 12 - 3 = \_\_$
$8 = 12 - \_\_ \to 12 - \_\_ = 8$
$7 = 12 - \_\_$ etc.
$9 = 13 - \_\_ \to 13 - 4 = \_\_$
$8 = 13 - \_\_ \to 13 - \_\_ = 8$
$7 = 13 - \_\_$ etc.

Step 5: Subtracting a 1-digit number from between 21 and 24 with a result less than 20

$19 = 21 - \_\_ \to 21 - \_\_ = 19$
$18 = 21 - \_\_ \to 21 - 3 = \_\_$
$17 = 21 - \_\_$ etc.
$19 = 22 - \_\_ \to 22 - 3 = \_\_$
$18 = 22 - \_\_ \to 22 - \_\_ = 18$
$17 = 22 - \_\_$ etc.
$19 = 23 - \_\_ \to 23 - 4 = \_\_$
$18 = 23 - \_\_ \to 23 - 5 = \_\_$
$17 = 23 - \_\_$ etc.

Step 6: Finding the difference between two numbers (working with the number 20)

$20 - 11$
(What is the difference between 20 & 11?)
$20 - 12$
(What is the difference between 20 & 12?)
$20 - 13$
(What is the difference between 20 & 13?)

Step 7: Finding the difference between two numbers (working between 21 and 24)

$21 - 11$ (What is the difference between 21 and 11?)
$21 - 12$ (the difference between 21 and 12?)
$21 - 13$, etc.
$22 - 11$ (the difference between 22 and 11?)
$22 - 12$ (the difference between 22 and 12?)
$22 - 13$, etc.
$23 - 11$ (the difference between 23 and 11?)
$23 - 12$ (the difference between 23 and 12?)
$23 - 13$, etc.

Class Two Maths

Overview of child development in Class Two

Class Two students are in the middle of an important developmental phase between the ages of six and nine. It is a golden time where they are still kings in their own kingdoms. They are now livelier and more aware of what is happening around them. They may even become mischievous. Physically, the roundness of the early childhood years has disappeared. The mouth is closed and the students become less dreamy. Their personality and character become more evident.

We can help the children to overcome the one-sidedness of their character by telling fables and saint stories. The joy of learning is based on strong habits, rhythms and songs. The creative forces of the child increase along with an ability to create more vivid inner pictures. Class Two students' confidence grows and builds upon the foundation laid in Class One. However, they still need strong leadership from the teacher through a consistent and rhythmical approach to the lessons. An artistic approach is used to awaken the intellect.

With the maths lessons, this is the year to introduce the times tables – all of them brought in an artistic way. The children are eager to show their individual abilities, such as the joy of finding missing numbers, or the discovery of geometrical patterns in the times tables. At this age, the children's memory forces are very strong, so it is an ideal time to begin to learn the arithmetic facts.

Curriculum summary for Class Two maths

The world of numbers
The children should become fluent with counting up to 100. They should be able to start anywhere and continue counting without any hesitation, and do this either counting forwards or backwards.

The students should gradually become at ease with the number world up to 1000 (and possibly higher).

Estimating. We build up from the estimating done in Class One and progress to more challenging estimates.

Place value
Place value is introduced and practised. Be sure that all the children really get this; this is an important step needed in order to deeply understand the world of numbers.

Addition and subtraction facts
By the end of the year, the class should have learned their addition facts (up to 24) and corresponding subtraction facts by heart.

The times/division tables

Beginning in Class Two, multiplication and division go together. The times tables and division tables are really the same thing.

By the end of the year, the class should be comfortable with all of the times and division tables (from 1 to 12), in a row. This requires daily, systematic work! Be sure to read *A step-by-step progression for the arithmetic facts* (p. 111 in the Appendix).

The four processes

Addition. By the end of the year, the class should be at ease with adding any 2-digit number with a 1-digit number (e.g. 57 + 6).

Subtraction. By the end of the year, the class should be at ease with subtracting any 1-digit number from a 2-digit number (e.g. 52 – 6), and also with subtracting two 2-digit numbers such that the answer is a 1-digit number (e.g. 72 – 69).

The students must gain a deeper understanding of the concept of *multiplication* and *division,* such as, $3 \times 2 = \rule{1em}{0.4pt}$ asks, 'Three groups of two makes what?' Or $12 \div 3 = \rule{1em}{0.4pt}$ asks, 'How many groups of three fit in twelve?'

By the end of the year, the children should be able to do *all four processes* (even alternating on the same page) and know the difference between the processes without help (but keep the problems simple).

The introduction to both vertical addition (carrying) and vertical subtraction (borrowing) should wait until Class Three. Therefore, all written work with the four processes should still be done in horizontal form (e.g. 9 = 5 + 4, 5 + 4 = 9).

Time orientation

The children should become at ease with the days of the week, the months of the year, and terms like 'tomorrow,' 'yesterday,' 'noon,' 'afternoon,' 'evening,' 'six o'clock,' etc.

The wonder of number

Bring wonder and awe to the world of numbers. One way in which this can be done is with the geometrical patterns that arise from the relation between times/division tables and the 10-point circle or the 12-point circle (see more details under Block 1, p. 57).

Recommended reading

Henning Anderson, *Active Arithmetic.*
Herman von Baravalle, *The Teaching of Arithmetic and the Waldorf School Plan.*
Else Göttgens, *Waldorf Education in Practice.*
Dorothy Harrer, *Maths Lessons for Elementary Grades.*
Christoph Jaffke, *Rhythms, Rhymes, Games and Songs for the Lower School.*
Lipping Ma, *Knowing and Teaching Elementary Mathematics.*
Ernst Schuberth, *Teaching Mathematics for First and Second Grades in Waldorf Schools.*
Heather Thomas, *A Journey Through Time.*
John A. van de Walle, *Elementary and Middle School Mathematics.*
Publication details: *Suggested Reading,* p. 125.

Lessons and topics for Class Two maths

Scheduling

The curriculum calls again for twelve weeks of maths. The first maths main lesson should fall around October, the second block around January, and the last block falls in the spring. Each block should be four weeks long, and there should be one week of maths review at the end of the school year.

Don't forget!

- Every day, we should *review* the previous day's lesson.
- Every day, we should *bring something new* to the children.
- Every day, the students should *practise the new material* and selected review topics.

Practice and review (of old material)

Most of the topics listed below were introduced some time ago. In order for the children to learn a topic well, it needs to be systematically reviewed. Obviously, all previous topics cannot be reviewed every day. The teacher needs to decide which topics are the most important. Some of these topics may need to be reviewed and practised nearly every day, even when the class is not in a maths block – although, it should take no more than a total of 10 minutes. (See also *Review and practice* under *Principles of Waldorf education* in the Introduction, p. 15.)

The world of numbers

Counting up to 100 fluently, and up to 1000 at ease – forwards and backwards. Children should be very comfortable in doing this on their own without help.

Number dictations should be used to help the students become familiar with the larger numbers that come about through the introduction of place value. Dictations should continue after the place value main lesson block ends. Students need to feel confident in writing any number between 1 and 1000.

Addition and subtraction facts

By the end of the year, the class should have learned their addition facts (up to 24) and corresponding subtraction facts by heart.

Strategies

Practise using strategies for addition and subtraction. For example, 24 + 13 can be looked at as 24 + 10 + 3 or 20 + 10 + 4 + 3 or 24 + 6 + 7, etc.

The times/division tables

Remember that times/division tables are the highest priority for maths in Class Two.

By the end of the year, the class should be comfortable with all of the times and division tables from 1 to 12, in a row. This requires daily, systematic work!

The times tables and the division tables are worked on at the same time. The students can then experience how multiplication and division are related. Be sure to read *A step-by-step progression for the arithmetic facts* (pp. 111f in the Appendix).

Practice with the four processes

The students should continue practising the four processes daily and develop strategies to solve these problems. The students need to practise a sufficient amount of problems, so that they start to feel confident. Also, try to make the problems interesting. For example, you could work it out so that there is a sequence in the answers, such as:

$18 + 17 = 35$
$21 + 14 = 35$
$29 + 6 = 35$

And then, there is suddenly a 'little dragon' that has a different answer!

$16 + 18 = 34$

Time

Once the weekdays, months, seasons and clock time have been covered in main lesson, they should all be reviewed at least briefly, so that the students remain fluent with these concepts.

Mental arithmetic

Practise mental arithmetic daily (for 10 minutes or less).

Mental arithmetic also helps the children to become flexible in using the four processes.

Work up to calculations like $28 + 5$, $14 \div 2$, 8×5, $86 - 3$, $76 - 74$, $42 - 6$, $72 - 69$.

Halfway problems. These problems should start off easy in Class Two and become increasingly difficult in the coming years. Some examples are:

- What number is halfway between 25 and 29?
- What number is halfway between 5 and 13?
- What number is halfway between 5 and 23?
- What number is halfway between 25 and 31?

Word problems

In Class Two, word problems may still be done through imaginative stories, and they can also be done more simply during the mental arithmetic section of the lesson. Here are some examples:

- An empty bus stops and picks up 8 people. At the next stop, 3 people get off and then 4 get on. How many people are now on the bus?
- A mother went to the market with her two children. They bought 24 oranges. They looked so delicious and all three of them ate one orange right away. On their way home, the children met a friend and all three children ate another orange. How many oranges were in the mother's basket when they got home?
- A father was working in the garden during autumn. He found a hole with 5 nuts in a tree, later he found 6 nuts buried in the ground, and then he found 8 nuts on a shelf in the garden shed. How many nuts were there in total?

Practice book

In Class Two, it is good for the children to keep a practice book. What has been done through movement exercises can now be written down. A practice book is very handy and helps the children learn how to organise their work. The work in this practice book should still be done neatly.

Maths main lesson block 1: Place value and the times tables

New material and content
The times tables
In this first maths block of Class Two, we begin to introduce the times and division tables.

Keep in mind that the goal is that by the end of the year, the class should be comfortable with all of the times tables from 1 to 12. This requires daily systematic work, and much careful planning.

Be sure to read *A step-by-step progression for the arithmetic facts* (pp. 111f in the Appendix).

Place value
It is best to work with images when introducing place value.

Gnomes and gems. We can create a story about a community of gnomes who are miners of gems. They need to find a way to keep track of the gems and count them. It may be good for the students to try first to come up with a system on their own. One idea is as follows: Groups of 10 gems are put into small pouches. Groups of 10 pouches are put into small buckets. Groups of 10 buckets are put into barrels, etc. In this way, the number 3785 is represented by 3 barrels, 7 buckets, 8 pouches, and 5 (single) gems. This is a nice story to illustrate in a main lesson book. It can lead into the next (perhaps less elaborate) story.

A woodcutter's mill. A woodcutter has a lumber mill that produces boards for sale in the village. Groups of 10 boards get tied into bundles. Groups of 10 bundles get put into crates. Groups of 10 crates get put onto horse wagons. In this way, the number 2497 is represented by two wagons, 4 crates, 9 bundles, seven (single) boards. This story nicely lends itself to the children practising place value by using craft (lollipop) sticks, which are available in most craft stores. You can simply give the students a large number of sticks, maybe around 2400 sticks, and have the students group them like the woodcutter so they can count all of the sticks.

After the introduction of place value, number dictations can help the students practise with these newly discovered larger numbers.

The four processes
Develop strategies for addition and subtraction. The students should be fluent with sums up to 24, and at ease up to 100. This work will continue throughout Class Two.

Movement
The circle of twelve
All of the times tables can come out of a twelve-circle. We like to introduce the circle of twelve because twelve represents a cosmic reality. The children are still very connected to the cosmos, the world they come from. The students

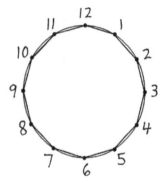

The 1 and 11 times table

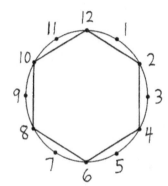

The 2 and 10 times table

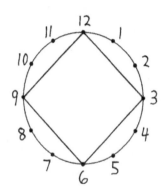

The 3 and 9 times table

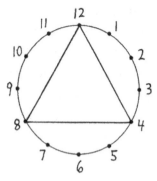

The 4 and 8 times table

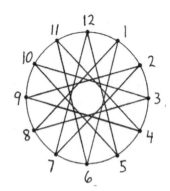

The 5 and 7 times table

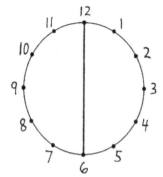

The 6 times table

will recognise the twelve in the clock, and in the twelve months (second block). We can do this for all of the times tables (starting with the two times table). For example, consider the five times table. The children sit on chairs in a circle, representing the numbers of the clock. Another child stands in the centre of the circle with a ball of yarn. The child representing the number 12 (which is also zero) holds one end of the yarn. The child in the centre takes 5 steps and ends up at the number 5. This child takes the string and everyone says, 'five equals one times five.' In this way, the middle child passes through the numbers of the fives times all the way up to 60 = 12 × 5. The yarn went around the circle several times. Once this is completed, we have woven together a beautiful twelve-pointed star.

The circle of ten*
The whole above process (just described with the twelve-circle) can also be done with the ten-circle. In this case, we start with a ten-

---

* We are presenting two options (the 12-circle and the 10-circle) for working with the times tables within a circle. We encourage the teacher to choose one option or the other. Doing both circles in Class Two is *not* recommended because it would be confusing to the students.

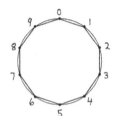 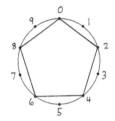 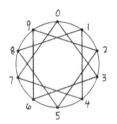  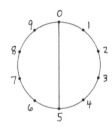

| The 1 and 9 × table | The 2 and 8 × table | The 3 and 7 × table | The 4 and 6 × table | The 5 times table |

pointed circle, where each child on the circle represents the digits zero to nine. The pattern we now get with the yarn follows the last digit of the chosen times table.

For example, using the four times table, the yarn is passed from the 4 (4 = 1 × 4), to the 8 (8 = 2 × 4), to the 2 (because in this third step, 12 = 3 × 4, which has 2 as a last digit), to the 6 (16 = 4 × 4), to the 0 (20 = 5 × 4), and then the digits repeat so the yarn revisits the same five children: 24 = 6 × 4; 28 = 7 × 4; 32 = 8 × 4; 36 = 9 × 4; 40 =10 × 4; 44 = 11 × 4; and finally 48 = 12 × 4. We have created a five-pointed star, which keeps repeating, again and again, no matter how far we choose to go – even if we went up to 100 = 25 × 4 we would get 5 five-pointed stars laid on top of one another.

Why do the four and six times tables produce the same geometrical pattern? Because they have similar qualities. The last digit for the four times table cycles every five steps (4, 8, 2, 6, 0), and the six times table has the same cycle, but backwards (6, 2, 8, 4, 0).

In the same way, the one, the nine and the eleven times tables all produce the same 10-sided figure (decagon); the two, eight and twelve times table all produce pentagons; and the three and the seven times tables both produce beautiful ten-pointed stars.

Of course, all of this can be quite an amazing discovery for Class Two children. They will come to the realisation that for any two numbers that add to ten, their tables will produce the same geometric pattern, but it is produced backwards. This is because the last digits in their tables follow the same pattern.

Stepping
Start at any given number between 100 and 1000 and have the whole class count forwards and backwards. Then do this in small groups and individually.

Clapping and stamping
This is important. Practise times tables with clapping and stamping in a rhythmical way. For example, using the four times table: four (clap hands) is (two hands on upper legs) one (clap hands) times (arms crossed) four (clap hands). There are many possibilities.

More ideas for movement
For more movement ideas see Henning Andersen's book, *Active Arithmetic*.

Working with manipulatives

Manipulatives should be used less frequently in Class Two than in Class One, but there are probably a few children who will still need the manipulatives (e.g. a string with beads).

The number line on the wall in the class can be used for games, etc. We can ask questions like: Where is the number that is 5 more than 26?

Board games can be fun, and some games with dice can help practise mental arithmetic. (See p. 111 in the Appendix for a list of games for lower school maths.)

Bookwork

The beautiful geometrical forms we created during our movement exercises (with either the twelve-circle or the ten-circle) can now be drawn into the children's main lesson books.

Visit *www.JamieYorkPress.com* to see full-colour pages from students' main lesson books.

Maths main lesson block 2: Time

New material and content

Time orientation

The main focus in this block is time: the days of the week, the months, and the clock. The children learn to read a clock with hands, where the minute hand is straight up on the 12, such as 4 o'clock, etc. We add the minutes in Class Three.

The times/division tables

The goal is that by the end of the year, the class should be comfortable with all of the times/division tables from 1 to 12. This requires daily systematic work, and much careful planning.

Be sure to read *A step-by-step progression for the arithmetic facts* (pp. 111f in the Appendix).

The four processes

We can slowly bring more difficult problems (but not too difficult!) to the children. Problems are presented both orally (with mental arithmetic) and in written form. Also, continue to develop strategies.

Place value

We should review and further what was introduced in the first block.

Number dictations

Number dictations should be done in order to help the students build an understanding of place value. With these number dictations we can vary the digits slightly, such as: 21, 12, 23, 32, 41, 14, 112, 121, 211, etc.

Making a calendar

It may be best if this block falls in January, which is a perfect time for making calendars.

Christoph Jaffke's book, *Rhythms Rhymes, Games and Songs for the Lower School*, has excellent poems for the theme of time and season. Heather Thomas's *A Journey Through Time* also has poems for numbers.

Don't forget to review and practise! Previously introduced material needs to be reviewed, practised, and furthered. (See *Practice and review* under *Lessons and topics for Class Two maths*, p. 54)

Movement

Movement exercises for the times tables
Continue to find interesting movement exercises for the times tables that use rhythm sticks, beanbags, and more.

Movement exercises for place value
The class teacher can find and invent a variety of games that practise place value.

Moving the four processes on the number line
For example, if you start at 38, and step forward by ten, where do you end up? And then, if you take another step? We can also do this with subtraction. This can also be helpful to develop strategies. For example, instead of stepping forward by 13, we first could take a step of ten followed by a step of three.

Moving with the clock
The clock can be visualised by making the circle with 12 students and the hour hand and minute hand can be two different students.

Moving with the weeks and months
We walk the days of the week and the months of the year forwards and backwards with the class, in small groups, and individually.

Working with manipulatives
Making a clock
The students can make a cardboard clock themselves, and then practise with it.

Bookwork
The students continue to put the times and division tables in their main lesson books in an artistic way.

Pictures of time. At 6 o'clock (morning) the sun comes up and we have breakfast; at 10 o'clock we have snack; at 12 o'clock (noon) the sun is overhead and we have lunch; at 6 o'clock the sun is setting as we eat, etc. The students can draw all of these pictures beautifully in their main lesson books.

The students can make a calendar with one page for each month. We can provide them with a pre-printed grid, which they can glue to a piece of paper. Every page has a poem of the month, and also has a drawing and includes the birthdays of their classmates.

Visit *www.JamieYorkPress.com* to see full-colour pages from students' main lesson books.

Maths main lesson block 3: Bringing it all together

New material and content

The major purpose of this main lesson block is to bring everything together that has been introduced previously. Of course, it is always best to find new variations to previously introduced material. New games (see the Appendix, p. 111 for a list of games for lower school maths), riddles and/or puzzles can be added.

The times tables

Finish the times and division tables up to 12 in an artistic way.

Keep in mind that the goal is that by the end of the year, the class should be comfortable with all of the times tables from 1 to 12 in a row. This requires daily systematic work, and much careful planning.

Be sure to read *A step-by-step progression for the arithmetic facts* (pp. 111f in the Appendix).

The children should create a times table square soon after all of the tables (1 to 12) have been introduced. This square should be done beautifully, with nice colours. The children can then try to find hidden secrets and patterns in the times table square.

The four processes

We continue to work with the four processes.

Ensure that the concepts of multiplication and division are clear.

Don't forget to review and practise! Previously introduced material needs to be reviewed, practised, and furthered. (See *Practice and review of old material* under *Lessons and topics for Class Two maths,* p. 54)

Movement

Rhythmical exercises

We should continue with daily rhythmical exercises, but we can now do more complicated movements for the times tables, and bring many variations.

For example, we could clap on the numbers that are in the two times table, and, at the same time, stamp our feet on the numbers that are in the three times table. All of this happens while we speak the numbers sequentially (see below, where *c* is clap, and *s* is stamp.) We can also use different percussion instruments.

1	2	3	4	5	6	7	8	9	10	11	12	13	14	15	16
	c	*s*	*c*		*cs*		*c*	*s*	*c*		*cs*		*c*	*s*	*c*

Working with manipulatives

Manipulatives are used less and less frequently. (See *Regarding number lines and manipulatives,* p. 33)

Bookwork

The children should finish their work with the times tables in their main lesson books.

The children can now put the times table square into their book. In many ways, this is the culmination of all of our work through the year with the times tables. It should be done very beautifully.

More ideas for Class Two maths

Be sure to reread the chapter, *Teaching Maths in Lower Classes,* found on p. 9 at the start of this book.

Commutative property

Years ago, schools taught the commutative property (e.g. 4 × 3 is the same as 3 × 4) and also the associative property – both in a very abstract way. There is, of course, no real reason to have the children become familiar with these terms, but we do want to look for opportunities for the children to discover the principles behind this. For the children, 5 × 3 (five groups of three) is a very different process than 3 × 5 (three groups of five). Likewise, 2 + 6 is a different process than 6 + 2, yet both yield the same sum. This can be an exciting 'aha' moment for the children when they discover for themselves that the two numbers being multiplied or added can be switched and the result will be the same.

Different kinds of subtraction

Three ways of looking at minus

There are (at least) three ways to look at a subtraction problem. (This is for the teacher to keep in mind; the students may not be fully conscious of this until Class Three.)

Using the example of 20 – 13:

As a take away (or subtraction) problem. We take away 13 from 20.

As a difference problem. We ask ourselves: 'How far apart are 13 and 20?' or 'How many steps are there going from 13 to 20?' This will be especially clear to the students once they have moved it on the number line.

As the reverse of addition. We ask ourselves: '13 plus what is 20?'

The goal is to develop flexibility in the children's thinking, so that sometimes they look at it as a difference problem, and sometimes as a take away problem, depending upon which approach is easier for a given problem.

The teacher should try to be consistent in the use of the words 'take away', 'difference', 'subtract', etc. By saying '26 minus 14', we leave it open for the children to solve the problem by either taking away or finding the difference.

The students should still be doing subtraction predominantly in the horizontal form (and in mental arithmetic) well into Class Three, and beyond.

No 'carrying' or 'borrowing' yet. It is best to delay vertical addition and subtraction until Class Three (see *Keep in the horizontal as much as possible* under *Developing a sense of number,* p. 26).

Step-by-step progressions

Addition

Of course, there are more steps possible than are listed opposite. This is intended to give the teacher some possible ideas of what could be done to work in a structured way.

It is important to remember that this is all 'mental arithmetic'. Vertical addition isn't introduced until Class Three.

Because these problems aren't done using vertical addition (i.e. carrying), this all lends itself to developing strategies. For example, after we have done quite a bit of this work, imagine all of the ways that a student could figure out 46 + 19?

The answer doesn't always have to appear at the end of the problem; it is important to vary the presentation of these problems, so that the students are flexible. For example, instead of $29 + 6 = \_\_$, we could write it as $29 + \_\_ = 35$.

It is important to find 'the story' behind a problem, or to 'translate' the problem into spoken language. For example, with $7 + \_\_ = 12$, I ask myself, 'How much do I need to add to 7 in order to get 12?' or 'Seven plus what makes twelve?', or 'What is the difference between 12 and 7?'

Step 1: Adding multiples of 10
$10 + 10 = \_\_ \rightarrow 20 = 10 + \_\_$
$20 + 10 = \_\_ \rightarrow 30 = 20 + \_\_$
$30 + 10 = \_\_$ etc.
$20 + 20 = \_\_ \rightarrow 40 = 20 + \_\_$
$30 + 20 = \_\_ \rightarrow 50 = 30 + \_\_$
$40 + 20 = \_\_$ etc.
$30 + 30 = \_\_ \rightarrow 60 = 30 + \_\_$
$40 + 30 = \_\_ \rightarrow 70 = 40 + \_\_$
$50 + 30 = \_\_$ etc.

Step 2: 2-digit plus 1-digit
(without carry)
$25 + 3 = \_\_ \rightarrow 28 = \_\_ + 3$
$36 + 2 = \_\_ \rightarrow 38 = \_\_ + 2$
$72 + 5 = \_\_ \rightarrow 77 = \_\_ + 5$ etc.

Step 3: Adding 10
$25 + 10 = \_\_ \rightarrow 35 = \_\_ + 10$
$36 + 10 = \_\_ \rightarrow 46 = \_\_ + 10$
$58 + 10 = \_\_ \rightarrow 68 = \_\_ + 10$
etc.

Step 4: 2-digit plus a multiple of 10
$25 + 30 = \_\_ \rightarrow 55 = \_\_ + 30$
$36 + 40 = \_\_ \rightarrow 76 = \_\_ + 40$
$58 + 20 = \_\_ \rightarrow 78 = \_\_ + 20$
etc.

Step 5: 2-digit number plus a number between 10 and 20 (without carrying)
$35 + 13 = \_\_ \rightarrow 48 = 35 + \_\_$
$74 + 12 = \_\_ \rightarrow 86 = 74 + \_\_$
$52 + 16 = \_\_ \rightarrow 68 = 52 + \_\_$
etc.

Step 6: 2-digit number plus a number between 10 and 20, and with units adding to 10
$44 + 16 = \_\_ \rightarrow 60 = 44 + \_\_$
$67 + 13 = \_\_ \rightarrow 80 = 67 + \_\_$
$63 + 17 = \_\_ \rightarrow 80 = 63 + \_\_$
$81 + 19 = \_\_ \rightarrow 100 = 81 + \_\_$
etc.

Step 7: 2-digit doubling
$24 + 24 = \_\_ \rightarrow 48 = \_\_ + \_\_$
$32 + 32 = \_\_ \rightarrow 64 = \_\_ + \_\_$
$45 + 45 = \_\_ \rightarrow 90 = \_\_ + \_\_$
$49 + 49 = \_\_ \rightarrow 98 = \_\_ + \_\_$
etc.

Step 8: Adding any two 2-digit numbers
The big, challenging step!

    $53 + 18 =$ ___ → $71 = 53 +$ ___
    $43 + 19 =$ ___ → $62 = 43 +$ ___
    $26 + 54 =$ ___ → $80 = 26 +$ ___
    $48 + 34 =$ ___ → $82 = 48 +$ ___
    etc.

Subtraction

Of course, there are more steps possible than are listed opposite. This is intended to give the teacher some possible ideas of what could be done to work in a structured way.

Remember that this is all 'mental arithmetic'. Vertical subtraction isn't introduced until Class Three.

Because these problems aren't done using vertical subtraction, this all lends itself to developing strategies. For example, after we have done quite a bit of this work, imagine all of the ways that a student could figure out $42 - 15$.

The answer doesn't always have to appear at the end of the problem; it is important to vary the presentation of these problems, so that the students are flexible. For example, instead of $29 - 6 =$ ___, we could write it as $29 -$ ___ $= 23$, or ___ $- 6 = 23$.

It is important to find 'the story' behind a problem, or to 'translate' the problem into spoken language. For example, with $17 = 22 -$ ___, I can ask: 'How many do I need to take away from 22 in order to get 17?'

Step 1: Subtracting multiples of 10
    $20 - 10 =$ ___ → $10 = 20 -$ ___
    $70 - 30 =$ ___ → $40 = 70 -$ ___
    $100 - 60 =$ ___ → $40 = 100 -$ ___
    etc.

Step 2: Subtracting 1-digit from 2-digits (without regrouping)
    $29 - 3 =$ ___ → $26 = 29 -$ ___
    $35 - 4 =$ ___ → $31 = 35 -$ ___
    $77 - 6 =$ ___ → $71 = 77 -$ ___
    etc.

Step 3: Subtracting 1-digit from 2-digits (with regrouping)
    $21 - 3 =$ ___ → $18 =$ ___ $- 3$
    $35 - 8 =$ ___ → $27 =$ ___ $- 8$
    $77 - 9 =$ ___ → $68 =$ ___ $- 9$
    etc.

Step 4: Subtracting two 2-digit numbers resulting in a 1-digit number (part I)
    $29 - 23 =$ ___ → $6 = 29 -$ ___
    $35 - 31 =$ ___ → $4 = 35 -$ ___
    $77 - 72 =$ ___ → $5 = 77 -$ ___
    etc.

Step 5: Subtracting two 2-digit numbers resulting in a 1-digit number (part II)
    $33 - 26 =$ ___ → $7 = 33 -$ ___
    $44 - 38 =$ ___ → $6 = 44 -$ ___
    $77 - 68 =$ ___ → $9 = 77 -$ ___
    etc.

A Teacher's Source Book for Mathematics in Classes 1 to 5

Step 6: Subtracting multiples of ten
   $33 - 10 = \underline{} \rightarrow 23 = 33 - \underline{}$
   $59 - 20 = \underline{} \rightarrow 39 = 59 - \underline{}$
   $87 - 40 = \underline{} \rightarrow 47 = \underline{} - 40$
   etc.

Step 7: Subtracting 11 to 19
without regrouping
   $48 - 15 = \underline{} \rightarrow 33 = 48 - \underline{}$
   $56 - 12 = \underline{} \rightarrow 44 = 56 - \underline{}$
   $97 - 16 = \underline{} \rightarrow 81 = 97 - \underline{}$
   etc.

Step 8: Subtracting 11 to 19 resulting
in a multiple of ten.
   $48 - 18 = \underline{} \rightarrow 30 = 48 - \underline{}$
   $56 - 16 = \underline{} \rightarrow 40 = 56 - \underline{}$
   $97 - 17 = \underline{} \rightarrow 80 = \underline{} - 17$
   etc.

Step 9: Subtracting 11 to 19 with
regrouping – developing strategies
   $53 - 18 = \underline{} \rightarrow 35 = 53 - \underline{}$
   (perhaps do $53 - 10 - 3 - 5$, or $53 - 20 + 2$)
   $82 - 14 = \underline{} \rightarrow 68 = 82 - \underline{}$
   $47 - 18 = \underline{} \rightarrow 29 = 47 - \underline{}$
   etc.

Step 10: Subtracting any two 2-digit numbers
These are the hardest problems!
   $53 - 38 = \underline{} \rightarrow 15 = 53 - \underline{}$
   $63 - 28 = \underline{} \rightarrow 35 = 63 - \underline{}$
   $87 - 38 = \underline{} \rightarrow 49 = 87 - \underline{}$
   etc.

Class Three Maths

Overview of child development in Class Three

The golden years come to an end as the children step out of their little kingdom. This is the nine-year change, which usually comes towards the end of Class Three. To the children, this can feel like a terrible loss and make them insecure. This is accompanied by a separation between the child and the world around. They can also feel that their teacher has changed. The children may become lonely, insecure and critical.

To help the children with this phase of their development we study the Old Testament. The order of law and lessons from the stories of the Hebrew people help to make the children feel more secure inwardly. Main lesson blocks like farming and house building help them to develop a new relationship with the world around them.

The eagerness to learn is still strong; this is a time of real blossoming. With the sturdy foundation of the first two classes, the children can apply their mathematical knowledge to practical, everyday situations. Once the students have the feeling that they are nourished, they become less anxious about stepping into this new phase of their life. For the teaching of maths, this means that we can bring them measurement and vertical arithmetic (carrying, long division, etc.). Having the children learn the arithmetic facts by heart is perhaps our most important goal.

Curriculum summary for Class Three maths

The world of numbers

The number world becomes fluent up to 1000 and at ease with the numbers up into the millions.

Number dictations should be continued in Class Three.

Place value work should be continued from Class Two, but now with larger numbers.

Learning all of the arithmetic facts

This is very important! Now is the time to learn the multiplication and division facts (that come from these tables) out of order. The groundwork was set in Class Two, when the children learned their times/division tables (from 1 to 12). Also, all of the addition and subtraction facts are reviewed and strengthened.

See *Arithmetic facts practice sheets*, p. 75, and *A step-by-step progression for the arithmetic facts* (p. 111 in the Appendix).

The four processes: working vertically

Before Class Three, the children have only been working with problems written horizontally.

Vertical addition. This is the first experience with working vertically. Slowly, build up to adding two 4-digit numbers. Vertical addition problems may be practised extensively.

Vertical subtraction. Perhaps, less time is spent here than on vertical addition. Don't make it too complicated; much more vertical subtraction practice will be done in Class Four.

Vertical multiplication. As with vertical subtraction, this could be just an introduction. In Class Three, vertical multiplication should be limited to single digit multipliers (i.e. 2347 × 5 might be the hardest). Don't overdo it! 2-digit multipliers should wait until Class Four.

Vertical division (long division). Class Three or Class Four? Vertical division (i.e. long division) is a very complicated procedure for many children. It requires division with remainders, multiplication, and subtraction. It requires that the children are fluent with their times/division tables. It requires the students to be systematic and organised in their work. For all of these reasons, each teacher needs to carefully consider whether the class is truly ready to be introduced to vertical division at the end of Class Three. It is probably best to wait until Class Four.

If vertical division is introduced in Class Three, then the division problems should be limited to two-step problems (e.g. 152 ÷ 4 = 38) that have divisors between 1 and 12. Keep it simple!

The four processes: working horizontally
Even though the children are being introduced to working with the four processes in vertical form, the bulk of their work with the four processes is still in horizontal form – as given on their arithmetic facts practice sheets.

We should begin practising horizontal division problems that result in a remainder (e.g. 46 ÷ 7).

Measurement
This is a fun, hands-on block! In this main lesson, we introduce time, distance, weight and volume.

Additionally, bartering and the use of money is handled in a simple and practical way.

Estimating is also an important part of this block.

Recommended reading
Henning Anderson, *Active Arithmetic.*
Herman von Baravalle, *The Teaching of Arithmetic and the Waldorf School Plan.*
Else Göttgens, *Waldorf Education in Practice.*
Dorothy Harrer, *Maths Lessons For Elementary Grades.*
Christoph Jaffke, *Rhythms, Rhymes, Games and Songs for the Lower School.*
Lipping Ma, *Knowing and Teaching Elementary Mathematics.*
Ernst Schuberth, *Teaching Mathematics for First and Second Grades in Waldorf Schools,* (especially the section about maths weaknesses, pp. 59ff).
Heather Thomas, *A Journey Through Time.*
John A. van de Walle, *Elementary and Middle School Mathematics.*
Publication details of the above titles are under *Suggested Reading,* p. 125.

Lessons and topics for Class Three maths

Scheduling

The curriculum calls again for twelve weeks of maths (three main lesson blocks of four weeks each), with one week of review at the end of the school year.

Don't forget:

- Every day, we should *review* the previous day's lesson.
- Every day, we should bring *something new* to the children.
- Every day, the students should *practise* the new material and selected review topics.

Practice and review of old material

Most of the topics listed below were introduced some time ago. In order for the children to learn a topic well, it needs to be systematically reviewed.

Obviously, all previous topics cannot be reviewed every day. The teacher needs to decide which topics are the most important. Some of these topics may need to be reviewed and practised nearly every day, whether the class is in a maths block, or not. As a general guideline, the class should practise 30 minutes daily when in a maths block, and about 10 minutes daily (in the morning) when not in a maths block. (Also see *Review and practice* under *Principles of Waldorf education*, p. 15.)

Daily practice sheets

This helps learning the arithmetic facts by heart.

The groundwork was set in Class Two when the children learned their times/division tables (1 to 12) in a row. They must now learn the multiplication and division facts (that come from these tables) out of order, as well as all of the addition facts and subtraction facts.

Remember that multiplication and division always go together. If we are working with a particular multiplication fact (for instance, $7 \times 4 = 28$) then we are working with the corresponding division fact ($28 \div 4 = 7$ and $28 \div 7 = 4$) at the same time. Additionally, facts should also be practised in a variety of different ways, such as $7 \times \_\_ = 28$, and $\_\_ \div 4 = 7$.

Be sure to read *Arithmetic facts practice sheets* under *More ideas for teaching Class Three maths*, p. 75. Also read *A step-by-step progression for the arithmetic facts* (p. 111 in the Appendix).

The times/division tables

Movement. Look at our example in Class Two, where we did the times table of two (with a clap) and three (with a stamp) while we counted. Now, we can add nodding our heads with the four times table. Henning Anderson gives several other good examples.

Every time we do a times table with movement exercises, we should also find a way of writing it into our main lesson books that shows the relationships.

Practice with the four processes

Even though the children in Class Three are being introduced to vertical arithmetic, they should still practise horizontal arithmetic (for instance, with their daily practice sheets). It is also important to keep up daily mental arithmetic (through to Class Eight). All of this helps ensure that their sense of number continues to develop and that they strengthen their ability to do simple calculations in their head.

We should continue to encourage the children to find strategies when working with the four processes.

We should begin to practise simple division problems that result in a remainder (like $46 \div 7$).

Mental arithmetic

Practise mental arithmetic daily (for 10 minutes or less), and continue to develop strategies through this work.

Work up to calculations like $46 + 5$; $28 + 31$; $75 - 68$; $73 - 4$; $24 \div 4$; $100 - 13$; $51 = 46 + \underline{\ \ }$.

Halfway problems. These problems should start off easy in Class Two, and now, in Class Three, can get a bit more challenging. Some examples are:

- What number is halfway between 25 and 41?
- What number is halfway between 25 and 61?
- What number is halfway between 250 and 450?

Word problems

Simple puzzles, riddles, and games can be valuable at this age (see *A list of Games,* p. 111 in the Appendix).

Reading clocks

In Class Two, the students were introduced to reading clocks (with hands), at least as far as reading times like 4 o'clock, 7 o'clock, etc. (where the minute hand is up at 12). Now, in Class Three, we learn to read all possible times, such as 5:23, 11:04, etc. We also cover the following: 4:30 is the same as 'half past four'; 8:45 is 'quarter to nine'; 10:50 is 'ten to eleven'; and 7:25 is 'about half past seven'.

Practice book

In Class Two, the children began to keep a practice book, which should be continued in Class Three and beyond. As always, the work in a practice book should be done neatly. In Class Three it teaches the children how to organise their work.

The world of numbers

We review counting up to 1000, and beyond, forwards and backwards. Number dictations should also be continued.

Maths main lesson block 1: Vertical addition and subtraction

New material and content

Vertical addition and subtraction
This is also known as 'carrying and borrowing'. It is a new (and exciting) subject.

This is just an introduction to vertical addition and subtraction. Over the course of the year, we will build up to adding two 4-digit numbers (like 8364 + 8375) and subtracting two 3-digit numbers (like 643 – 387).

Terminology. Try not to use the word 'borrowing' with the students because we never actually give anything back in the process. (Here we will call the whole procedure 'vertical subtraction', and the strategy that gets us around the tricky situation where, in a given column, the top digit is smaller than the bottom digit we will call 'regrouping'.)

The students first need to be confident with place value. Therefore, a strong review of Class Two place value will be necessary. It is wise to also review the regrouping of numbers.

For example, how can we regroup 53 as the sum of two numbers? It could be written as 53 = 50 + 3, or 53 = 40 + 13, or 53 = 30 + 23, or 53 = 52 + 1, or 53 = 48 + 5, etc.

Read *A step-by-step progression* under *More ideas for teaching Class Three maths,* p. 73.

Don't forget to review and practise! Previously introduced material needs to be reviewed, practised, and furthered (see *Practice and review of old material,* p. 68).

Movement

The times tables should now be done with more challenging movement. Different times tables could be 'moved' at the same time.

Example: We can clap the two, stamp the three, and move our head on the six.

Example: With the 3, 6, 9 and 12 tables, have one student count, perhaps by beating a drum, and assign the rest of the class different tables (3, 6, 9, 12). Different movements are assigned to each table. Perhaps the phlegmatics should have the 3 times table, so that they move the most.

After doing such exercises, we should ask the class some questions, such as: When did we all move at the same time? When did only the nines move? When was there no movement?

Try to find many more ways of bringing movement to the times tables so that the class can work together in a joyful way.

Working with manipulatives

Students should now be able to imagine the regrouping of the numbers, therefore manipulatives should be avoided.

Bookwork

The students should add many vertical addition and subtraction problems into their books.

The work needs to be neat and orderly. Use appropriate colours (e.g. green for adding and blue for subtracting, etc.).

Visit *www.JamieYorkPress.com* to see full-colour pages from students' main lesson books.

Maths main lesson block 2: Measurement

New material and content

Measurement is the main theme of the main lesson.

Linear measurement

The children are introduced to linear measurement through hands-on experiences based on the human body, like a (hand) span, cubit (from elbow to fingertip) and foot.

These human measures were standardised into the old British (imperial) measures, some of which are still used today (like mile).

Many teachers only introduce the more abstract metric system in Class Four.

The students should measure things in and around the classroom.

As a class we can make a simple graph that shows one particular student's height over a period of several months – or maybe everyone could do that for themselves at home.

Weight

Weight should also be part of the experience. The students can weigh objects in the classroom, and they can weigh one another.

Volume and liquid measure

With liquid measure we should pour cups into buckets, tablespoons into a cup, etc. Some teachers only introduce weight and volume measure in Class Four.

Origins. The historical origins of various units of measurement can be brought in an imaginative way (for instance, through the story of Noah's Ark).

Practical use. Of course, it is best to show practical uses of measurement, such as with simple building projects, cooking recipes, etc.

Estimating. The students should practise estimating. For example, they could estimate the length of a board, the height of a tree, the distance between two rocks, the weight of an animal. We should always try to estimate before taking an actual measurement.

Unit conversions. The students should practise very simple unit conversions, such as converting centimetres to metres (or, if the imperial measures have been sufficiently covered, feet to yards, or feet to inches).

Money

This is also the time to introduce the children to our currency. They can make their own money (coins and notes) and stock a shop, or even create a market place. We can also create games for money. Through all of this activity, the children practise counting money and giving change.

Vertical addition and subtraction

Vertical addition and subtraction was introduced in the first maths block of Class Three. In the meantime, this new material has been 'put to sleep' (see *The conscious use of forgetting* under *Principles of Waldorf Education*, p. 14).

It is important that we do not touch upon new material in between two maths blocks. Now that the material (vertical addition and subtraction) has had its proper 'rest', we can review it and then deepen it.

Division with remainders
This should be done using the same dividend but different divisors. For example, using the number 14, divide it by 1, 2, 3, etc. ($14 \div 1 =$ ___ ; $14 \div 2 =$ ___ ; $14 \div 3 =$ ___ ; $14 \div 4 =$ ___ , etc.) After some time, the students will improve at figuring out the remainder. This is preparation for vertical (long) division.

Don't forget to review and practise
Previously introduced material needs to be reviewed, practised and furthered (see *Practice and review of old material*, p. 68.)

Movement
Continue the movement activities that were done in the first block.

Working with manipulatives
Of course, there are unlimited possibilities for hands-on experiences and activities during this measurement block. This should bring a lively spirit to the lessons and enthuse the students.

Many props and visual aids are helpful for this block. For example, with volumes we could use milk cartons, jugs, bottles, spoons, cups, cans, etc.

Our work with money and currency lends itself nicely to working with manipulatives.

Bookwork
The children should write what they have experienced (for instance, the height of a chair is one cubit, etc.) in their main lesson books. They can make drawings (e.g. of a foot) as it applies to the units of measurement.

Visit *www.JamieYorkPress.com* to see full-colour pages from students' main lesson books.

Maths main lesson block 3: Vertical multiplication (and division)

New material and content
Vertical multiplication
Vertical multiplication can only be successful when the students feel confident with the times tables.

In Class Three, vertical multiplication should be limited to single digit multipliers (2347×5 might be the hardest). Don't overdo it! 2-digit multipliers should wait until Class Four.

Read *A step-by-step progression for vertical multiplication*, p. 74.

Vertical (long) division
Every teacher needs to carefully consider whether the class is truly ready to be introduced to vertical division at the end of Class Three, or whether it is best to wait until Class Four.

If it is decided to introduce vertical division at the end of Class Three, then keep these things in mind:

- Keep it simple! The problems should be limited to two-step problems (that is, 2-digit answers like $152 \div 4 = 38$) having divisors between 1 and 12.
- Keep it brief! Be sure that the class doesn't get overwhelmed with too many vertical division problems. A brief introduction should be enough.
- Read the sections on vertical division found in the *Class Four* chapter of this book, including: *Working vertically (division)* p. 82, and *A step-by-step progression for vertical division*, pp. 91f.

Don't forget to review and practise! Previously introduced material needs to be reviewed, practised, and furthered (see *Practice and review of old material*, p. 68).

Movement

It is a challenging but important task to bring all the times tables together in movement. Here is one idea of how it could be done, where the children are the workers on a ship.

The captain counts the ones; the twos are sweeping the deck; the threes throw the buckets of water on the deck; the fours raise the sails; the fives pull up the anchor, etc.

Groups move and speak when they hear a number from their times table.

It is fine if some students only observe, since there are several questions that can be asked at the end of the exercise (e.g. When did we hear only the captain? When was the whole crew moving and speaking?, etc.).

Working with manipulatives

We recommend keeping away from manipulatives during this vertical multiplication main lesson. The students need to internalise the processes.

Bookwork

The children can include several examples (some with all of the steps) of vertical multiplication (and vertical division?) in their main lesson book.

Visit *www.JamieYorkPress.com* to see full-colour pages from students' main lesson books.

More ideas for teaching Class Three maths

Be sure to reread the chapter, *Teaching Maths in Lower Classes*, p. 9 at the start of this book.

Step-by-step progressions

Vertical addition and subtraction

Step 1: 2-digit addition/subtraction without carrying or borrowing

Many of these problems should be done during the first maths block of Class Three.

$$
\begin{array}{rcl}
35 & \rightarrow & 30 + 5 \\
+14 & \rightarrow & +(10 + 4) \\
\hline
49 & \leftarrow & 40 + 9
\end{array}
$$

$$
\begin{array}{rcl}
56 & \rightarrow & 50 + 6 \\
-23 & \rightarrow & -(20 + 3) \\
\hline
33 & \leftarrow & 30 + 3
\end{array}
$$

Step 2: Using and showing regrouping strategies
Many of these problems should be done during the first maths block of Class Three.

```
  46  →    40 + 6
 +38  →  +(30 + 8)
 ─────    ──────────
  84  ←    70 +14
```

```
  83  →    70 + 13
 −25  →  −(20 + 5)
 ─────    ──────────
  58  ←    50 + 8
```

It is important that the children have worked a good deal with regrouping strategies (but not with vertical arithmetic) beginning in Class Two.

Step 3: The short cut – standard, vertical addition and subtraction
Many of these problems should be done during the second maths block of Class Three.

Using the same examples as above:

```
   1                    7
  46                   83
 +38                  −25
 ────                 ────
  84                   58
```

In order to make these problems more meaningful, try creating problems that relate to various activities.

It is best to introduce vertical addition and subtraction in an artistic way. For example, with vertical addition, we can draw a house where there is a level for every number. The answer ends up in the basement, and the attic is used for the 'carry' numbers. This should not be too elaborate of a story; it is simply an artistic way of writing it down.

Something similar can also be done for vertical subtraction.

Visit *www.JamieYorkPress.com* to see full-colour drawings of all of this.

Vertical multiplication (with single-digit multipliers)
Step 1: Write down familiar multiplication facts in vertical form

```
   4
  ×7
  ──
  28
```

Step 2: A 2-digit number (in expanded form) times a single-digit number.

```
 24  →  20 + 4   (The 2-digits are regrouped)
 ×6  →   ×   6
         ─────────
          24
        + 120
        ───────
          144
```

Step 3: The short cut – standard, vertical multiplication (again, 2-digit times 1-digit)

```
   2
  24
 ×  6
 ────
 144
```

Step 4: A 3-digit number (in expanded form) times a single-digit number.

```
 486  →  400 + 80 + 6
 × 3  →  ____ ____ × 3
                   ──────
                      18
                     240
                 +  1200
                 ────────
                    1458
```

A Teacher's Source Book for Mathematics in Classes 1 to 5

Step 5: The short cut – standard, vertical multiplication (again, 3-digit times 1-digit)

```
  2 1
  486
 ×  3
 1458
```

Step 6: Without writing down the carry digit

```
  486
 ×  3
 1458
```

It is important for the students to work towards not writing down the carry digit (that is, holding the carry digit in their head).

Arithmetic facts practice sheets

You can download Class Three arithmetic facts practice sheets free from *www.JamieYorkPress.com/downloads/* (under the '3rd Grade' label).*

Facts of the week
The central idea of these sheets is that there are five facts of the week (see p. 77) written on the board, which the teacher works on with the whole class during the week in a variety of ways (for instance, using movement, rhythmical work, games, etc.). These facts of the week then appear multiple times on the sheets for the current week, and are then reviewed systematically for the next several weeks.

* Depending on your printer, you may need to reformat the file to print on A4 pages.

Background work
These sheets should ideally be the culmination of two years of work. If the work in Classes One and Two has been effective, then the children should feel that these sheets are easy. If these sheets become too difficult and tedious, then it is likely that the classroom work being done in preparation for these sheets is either insufficient or not effective enough.

Timing and rhythm
The intention is that the first Class Three arithmetic facts practice sheet should be done at some point between the end of September and the end of October in Class Three. It can, of course, vary depending upon the class. After that, a sheet should be done (nearly) every day until the whole set of 100 sheets is completed. There are 20 weeks (100 days) of sheets in this set. Each sheet has 30 problems.

Completion
Since these sheets are designed to be an integral part of learning the maths facts, it is important that each sheet of the entire set be completed, otherwise certain facts won't get adequate exposure.

Caution! This should be fun and easy for the students. If successful, this builds their confidence. It is important to make sure that these sheets don't become torture for the students. Try to de-emphasise the importance of speed. Help the students to realise that improvement is what is important.

The whole picture

The 30 problems listed on a particular sheet are only a part of the daily maths practice. It would be very unfortunate if daily maths practice consisted of nothing more than the 30 arithmetic facts practice problems that appear on these sheets.

When the class is not in a maths main lesson, daily maths practice should take about 10 minutes. The 30 arithmetic facts may take 3 to 5 minutes. The remaining 5 to 7 minutes can be spent doing a few written (vertical) arithmetic problems, some brief rhythmical work, or something else.

When the class is in a maths main lesson, daily maths practice should take about 30 minutes. The 30 arithmetic facts may take 3 to 5 minutes. After that, the remaining 25 minutes of maths practice (during a maths main lesson) consists of the material that was brought in previous blocks and the current block.

The elements of maths practice

The following list shows some of the aspects to consider when planning maths practice for the day.

Arithmetic facts practice sheet. The teacher copies by hand the 30 problems from our practice sheets onto paper to be photocopied (about 5 minutes).*

---

* Try to find ways to reduce the amount of paper being used. For example, rather than using one sheet of paper each day, each side could be divided into three columns (i.e., 1 sheet = 6 days). This is one way to help develop an environmental consciousness in the students.

Mental arithmetic. The teacher may decide to read the first 6 problems out loud.

Extra maths practice problems. There should be a few extra problems that the teacher comes up with and writes on the board. The students copy them into their practice books and work out the answers. These problems also include practice and review of material covered in previous maths blocks. (Takes 20 to 25 minutes if the class is in a maths block, otherwise only 5 minutes.)

Challenge problems. It is important that the last few problems (that the teacher adds on) be more challenging in order to keep the 'quicker' students fully engaged.

What comes next?

The next set of practice sheets is titled *Arithmetic Facts Review Sheets (4th Grade)* and is intended to thoroughly review the maths facts covered on the first practice sheets.

The hope is that just five minutes per day of practising these arithmetic facts results in the whole class quite effortlessly learning their maths facts by heart.

And what happens if... ?

We hope that it won't happen, but there may be a few children at the end of Class Three who still haven't solidly learned their arithmetic facts. In order to help these children, we can give them a multiplication/division table (a square for the tables). Additionally, these students could study the basic arithmetic problems with flashcards during morning practice time.

The 105 key arithmetic facts

Each appears as a 'fact of the week'

8 + 2	6 + 6	11 − 9	13 − 9	16 − 9	4 × 4	6 × 6
9 + 2	7 + 6	11 − 8	13 − 8	16 − 8	4 × 5	6 × 7
7 + 3	8 + 6	11 − 7	13 − 7	16 − 7	4 × 6	6 × 8
8 + 3	9 + 6	11 − 6	13 − 6	17 − 9	4 × 7	6 × 9
9 + 3	7 + 7	11 − 5	13 − 5	17 − 8	4 × 8	6 × 12
6 + 4	8 + 7	11 − 4	13 − 4	18 − 9	4 × 9	7 × 7
7 + 4	9 + 7	11 − 3	14 − 9		4 × 12	7 × 8
8 + 4	8 + 8	11 − 2	14 − 8	3 × 3	5 × 5	7 × 9
9 + 4	9 + 8	12 − 9	14 − 7	3 × 4	5 × 6	7 × 12
5 + 5	9 + 9	12 − 8	14 − 6	3 × 5	5 × 7	8 × 8
6 + 5	10 − 8	12 − 7	14 − 5	3 × 6	5 × 8	8 × 9
7 + 5	10 − 7	12 − 6	15 − 9	3 × 7	5 × 9	8 × 12
8 + 5	10 − 6	12 − 5	15 − 8	3 × 8	5 × 12	9 × 9
9 + 5	10 − 5	12 − 4	15 − 7	3 × 9		9 × 12
	10 − 4	12 − 3	15 − 6	3 × 12		11 × 11
	10 − 3					11 × 12
	10 − 2					12 × 12

Facts of the week

Week 1: 8 + 2; 7 + 3; 6 + 4; 9 + 2; 9 + 3; 9 + 4;
9 + 5; 9 + 6; 9 + 7; 9 + 8

Week 2: 5 + 5; 6 + 6; 7 + 7; 8 + 8; 9 + 9

Week 3: 10 − 8; 10 − 7; 10 − 6; 3 × 3; 3 × 4

Week 4: 8 + 3; 7 + 4; 6 + 5; 10 − 5; 3 × 8

Week 5: 8 + 4; 7 + 5; 10 − 4; 10 − 3; 10 − 2

Week 6: 8 + 5; 7 + 6; 11 − 9; 12 − 9; 13 − 9

Week 7: 8 + 6; 8 + 7; 14 − 9; 15 − 9; 3 × 7

Week 8: 16 − 9; 17 − 9; 18 − 9; 3 × 9; 4 × 5

Week 9: 11 − 8; 13 − 8; 3 × 6; 4 × 4; 5 × 5

Week 10: 11 − 4; 12 − 8; 13 − 4; 3 × 5; 5 × 6

Week 11: 11 − 7; 12 − 5; 16 − 7; 3 × 12; 5 × 8

Week 12: 12 − 3; 13 − 7; 14 − 7; 4 × 7; 5 × 7

Week 13: 11 − 5; 13 − 5; 17 − 8; 4 × 9; 5 × 12

Week 14: 12 − 4; 14 − 6; 15 − 6; 4 × 8; 5 × 9

Week 15: 11 − 6; 13 − 6; 14 − 5; 7 × 8; 4 × 6

Week 16: 11 − 2; 12 − 6; 15 − 7; 6 × 9; 6 × 12

Week 17: 11 − 3; 14 − 8; 15 − 8; 6 × 7; 6 × 6

Week 18: 12 − 7; 16 − 8; 6 × 8; 7 × 7; 7 × 9

Week 19: 4 × 12; 8 × 8; 8 × 9; 11 × 11; 9 × 9

Week 20: 8 × 12; 9 × 12; 7 × 12; 11 × 12; 12 × 12

Class Four Maths

Overview of child development in Class Four

The gates of paradise have closed; the child has arrived on the earth. Steiner referred to this age (Classes Four and Five) as the 'heart of childhood'. In Class Four, the children start to find their way in the world. Their interactions with peers and adults can be challenging. They want to know more about the world, about personalities, and about good and evil. The stories of Norse mythology are a great help with this, and the children are eager to learn all about it.

Local geography helps the students to orientate themselves in space. They are introduced to grammar, singing in rounds, and musical notation. And in maths, one of the most difficult concepts is introduced – fractions. The beautiful world of ONE falls to pieces, while they discover that there exists a new world of numbers in between any two whole numbers.

Curriculum summary for Class Four maths

The world of numbers
Greatest common factors (GCF) should be introduced and practised.
Least common multiples (LCM) should be introduced and practised. This is needed as preparation for finding common denominators with fractions.

The arithmetic facts
Keeping it fresh. If all went well in Class Three, then the whole class should be quite solid with their arithmetic facts. In Class Four, we simply need to keep it fresh. Our Class Four arithmetic facts review sheets may only be needed two or three times per week (depending upon the class). Oral mental arithmetic also helps to keep the arithmetic facts fresh (see *Arithmetic facts review sheets*, p. 89, and *A step-by-step progression for the arithmetic facts*, pp. 111f in the Appendix).

Challenging multiplication facts. The teacher can select some challenging multiplication facts from the 13 through to the 25 times tables. Some of these can be done by the whole class, and some can be given just to those students needing an extra challenge. This work can be continued into Classes Five and Six.

The four processes
Horizontal addition and subtraction. It is still good for the students to practise strategies (perhaps learned in earlier classes) for addition and subtraction with numbers up to 1000. They should become fluent working out problems like: 125 + 126, 895 + 112, 974 – 875. This can either be done through written practise or as oral mental arithmetic.
Vertical addition and subtraction. This was introduced in Class Three, but now, in Class Four, we work with larger numbers. Regular practise is needed.

Vertical multiplication. In Class Three, we worked with single-digit multipliers. Now we can practise with 2-digit and 3-digit multipliers. Regular practice (but not too much!) is needed.

Vertical division (long division). Class Four is the time to introduce vertical division (unless it was briefly introduced in Class Three). Through the year, we can build up to 4-step problems (or 4-digit answers), but keep the divisors between 2 and 12 (e.g. $15,288 \div 6$). Regular practice (but not too much!) is needed.

Measurement

We should review Class Three measurement, and introduce the metric system. Some teachers only do weight and volume measure in Class Four.

Fractions

The goal in Class Four is for the children to develop a sense for fractions – to bring them to an understanding of what a fraction is. Too much of an emphasis on procedural skills will probably overwhelm many of the students, make it harder for them to develop a sense for fractions, and leave them hating fractions.

By the end of Class Four, the students should have a basic understanding of fractions, including problems similar to those found in the following list. Again, keep it simple!

- Give two other fractions that are equivalent to two thirds.
- What is $\frac{1}{5}$ of 35? What is $\frac{2}{3}$ of 12?
- Mr Jones has twenty students in his class.

If one quarter of the class is outside, then how many students are outside?

- How can two apples be divided fairly between four people? Between six people?
- The students should become at ease with fraction problems like these:

$$\tfrac{3}{5} + \tfrac{1}{5} = \underline{}$$

$$\tfrac{5}{6} + \tfrac{1}{2} = \underline{}$$

$$1\tfrac{1}{6} + \tfrac{4}{6} = \underline{}$$

$$\tfrac{7}{12} - \tfrac{3}{12} = \underline{}$$

$$\tfrac{3}{4} - \tfrac{1}{3} = \underline{}$$

$$1\tfrac{5}{8} - \tfrac{6}{8} = \underline{}$$

$$\tfrac{3}{5} \times \tfrac{1}{2} = \underline{}$$

$$\tfrac{2}{3} \times \tfrac{1}{2} = \underline{}$$

$$5 \div \tfrac{1}{4} = \underline{}$$

$$\tfrac{1}{4} \div \tfrac{1}{12} = \underline{}$$

Types of fractions. Although proper (i.e. 'normal') fractions receive the most attention, improper fractions and mixed numbers should also be introduced.

Equivalent fractions. The students should clearly understand the idea of equivalent fractions (e.g. that $\frac{3}{4}$ is the same as $\frac{6}{8}$).

Common denominators are introduced, and by the end of the year, the students should be at ease with them.

With fractions, we work from the whole to the parts, and from the parts to the whole.

All four processes with (simple, proper) fractions should be introduced.

Recommended reading

Henning Anderson, *Active Arithmetic.*

Herman von Baravalle, *The Teaching of Arithmetic and the Waldorf School Plan.*

Dorothy Harrer, *Maths Lessons For Elementary Grades.*

Christoph Jaffke, *Rhythms, Rhymes, Games and Songs for the Lower School.*

Ron Jarman, *Teaching Mathematics in Rudolf Steiner Schools for Classes I-VIII,* (recommended for ideas for Class Four and up.)

Lipping Ma, *Knowing and Teaching Elementary Mathematics.*

Heather Thomas, *A Journey Through Time.*

John A. van de Walle, *Elementary and Middle School Mathematics.*

Publication details of the above titles are under *Suggested Reading,* p. 125.

Lessons and topics for Class Four maths

Scheduling

The curriculum calls again for twelve weeks of maths (three main lesson blocks of four weeks each), with one week of review at the end of the school year.

Don't forget:

- Every day, we should *review* the previous day's lesson.
- Every day, we should bring *something new* to the children.
- Every day, the students should *practise* the new material and selected review topics.

Practice and review of old material

During each maths main lesson, we should be sure to practise the material from previous blocks and previous classes for at least half an hour every day.

Most of the topics listed below were introduced some time ago. In order for the children to learn a topic well, it needs to be systematically reviewed. Obviously, all previous topics cannot be reviewed every day. The teacher needs to decide which topics are the most important. Some of these topics may need to be reviewed and practised nearly every day, whether the class is in a maths block, or not. As a general guideline, the class should practise 30 minutes daily, when in a maths block, and about 10 minutes daily (in the morning) when not in a maths block. (Also see *Review and practice* under *Principles of Waldorf education,* p. 15.)

Regarding Class Four fractions

Caution! Often in Waldorf circles, you hear it said regarding the maths curriculum, that 'Class Four is fractions'. It is true that the introduction to fractions is an important part of the Class Four year. However, in terms of classroom time spent in maths lessons, work with fractions should not dominate everything else. Review and practice of concepts introduced in Class Three, such as measurement and vertical arithmetic, is very important, as well as continued practice with horizontal arithmetic.

Keep it simple! Everything listed here (for Class Four) is intended as part of an introduction to fractions. There will be much more work with fractions in the coming years.

It is not yet the goal to develop mastery of fraction skills – much of this is done in Classes Five and Six. Too much of an emphasis on procedural skills with fractions will probably overwhelm many of the students, make it harder for them to develop a sense for fractions, and leave them hating fractions.

The goal in Class Four is for the children to develop a sense for fractions – to bring them to an understanding of what a fraction is. This is the foundation for studying fractions in future years.

The world of numbers

Greatest common factor (GCF). For example, we can ask, 'What is the GCF of 30 and 24?' They then make one list of the factors of 24 (which are 1, 2, 3, 4, 6, 8, 12, 24), and another list of the factors of 30 (which are 1, 2, 3, 5, 6, 10, 15, 30). We can then see that the common factors are: 1, 2, 3, 6, and that 6 is the GCF. After some practice, they should be able to do simple GCF problems in their heads.

Least common multiple (LCM). For example, we can ask, 'What is the LCM of 4 and 6?' They then make a list of the multiples of 4 (i.e. numbers that are in the 4 times table), and another list of the multiples of 6. They can then see that 12 is the LCM. After some practice, they should be able to do simple LCM problems in their heads. A good amount of LCM practice should happen

before the second fraction main lesson when finding least common denominators is important.

Number dictations should still happen occasionally in Class Four. The children should be fluent with writing and reading numbers well into the millions. We can include fractions in our number dictations.

Place value can be briefly reviewed and practised.

Arithmetic facts

Even if all went well in Class Three with the learning of the arithmetic facts, there is still much work to be done in Class Four, so that the facts are not forgotten. They should be practised briefly, nearly every day, either through oral mental arithmetic, or with written practice sheets. Arithmetic facts review sheets are available as free downloads from *www.JamieYorkPress.com*.

Division with remainders. This was begun in Class Three. For example, we can give 33 ÷ 6, and their answer should be '5 with a remainder of 3'. We could also tell the students to take some number (e.g. 30) and divide it by 1, 2, 3, 4, etc. They can discover patterns with this.

Challenging multiplication facts. The teacher can select some challenging multiplication facts from the 13 through to the 25 times tables. Some of these can be done by the whole class, and some can be given just to those students needing an extra challenge. This work can be continued into Classes Five and Six.

The arithmetic facts can now be practised in a more challenging way. For example, we can toss a beanbag or a tennis ball to a student as we call out a number. The student then answers with a multiplication or division fact while throwing the ball back. For example, if the teacher says 28, then the student could give a variety of answers, such as: 2×14, 14×2, 7×4, 28×1, or $56 \div 2$, $112 \div 4$ etc. After working with one number, the students can write down all the different possibilities for that number.

Working horizontally
We should practise strategies (perhaps learned in earlier classes) for addition and subtraction, with numbers up to 1000. The students should become fluent with problems like $125 + 126$, $895 + 112$, $974 - 875$. This can either be done through written practice sheets or with oral mental arithmetic.

Working vertically
Every day, we should practise vertical addition, subtraction, multiplication and division. However, keep in mind that some students will slowly, over time, gain mastery over vertical arithmetic. Be sure that these students don't become anxious about it; they should still be learning joyfully!

Vertical addition and subtraction
This is continued from what was done in Class Three, but now with larger numbers. Regular practice is needed.

Vertical multiplication
In Class Three, we worked with single-digit multipliers. Starting in the second maths block of Class Four, we can practise with 2-digit and 3-digit multipliers. Regular practice is needed.

Be sure to read *A step-by-step progression for vertical multiplication* under *More ideas for teaching Class Four maths*, p. 91.

Vertical (long) division
Probably vertical division is new in Class Four. Over the course of the year, we can build up to 4-step problems (that is, with 4-digit answers), but keep the divisors between 2 and 12 (e.g. $15{,}288 \div 6$). 2-digit divisors (e.g. $1909 \div 23$) should wait until Class Five.

It can be helpful to introduce vertical division with a story, but be careful that the stories are not too elaborate, and that the details are relevant to the mathematical concepts.

Vertical division doesn't have to be a blind procedure. The children can be shown, to some degree, why it works. Be sure to read *A step-by-step progression for long division* under *More ideas for teaching Class Four maths*, pp. 91f.

Teach that maths is flexible! Students should feel that there are different ways to solve a given maths problem, even though showing multiple methods may not always be practical. In the case of vertical division, it is good to show different methods to the students. Parents, who are from different countries, can show the class how they learned to do division. The students don't need to understand these different methods, but they can appreciate that other methods exist.

When the children begin practicing vertical division, it is necessary to lead them step-by-step through the procedure.

The sequential steps in long division are as follows (using the two-step division example $152 \div 4$):

- First, we ask: 'How many times does 4 go into 15?' (Answer: 3)
- Multiply 3×4 and then write it under the 15.
- Subtract to get a remainder of 3.
- Bring down the next digit.
- Repeat the above process until the problem is finished.

$$
\begin{array}{r}
38 \\
4\overline{)152} \\
-12 \\
\hline
32 \\
-32 \\
\hline
0
\end{array}
$$

We should try to be very consistent and formulate the same questions during the process each time we do a long division problem.*

Once again, be sure that the class doesn't get overwhelmed with too many vertical division problems that are too difficult. It will be practised much more in Classes Five and Six.

Check answers to division problems by multiplying (e.g. for $2292 \div 6 = 382$, multiply 6×382 to make sure that it's equal to 2292).

---

* Herman von Baravalle, *The Teaching of Arithmetic and the Waldorf School Plan.*

Mental arithmetic

Practise mental arithmetic daily (for 10 minutes or less), and continue to develop strategies.

Work up to calculations like: $400 - 12$; $798 + 5$; 3×400; 28×100; $1000 - 25$; $3000 - 205$; $8000 - 2700$; 40×70; 300×5.

'Halfway' problems. Simple variations of these problems may have been introduced in Classes Two and Three, but now we can include more complicated variations, like:

- What number is halfway between 14 and 32?
- What number is halfway between 16 and 86?
- What number is halfway between 250 and 350?
- What number is halfway between 250 and 280?
- What is halfway between 600 and 1200?
- What is halfway between 600 and 1100?
- What number is halfway between 25 and 30?

In Class Four, it can be helpful (and fun!) to ask the students to find as many strategies as possible. Here are a few possible strategies (using the example 'What's halfway between 14 and 32?'):

Estimate and check. Estimate the answer, check it, and adjust until you finally get it. (This is probably what most students try to do at first.) With the given example ('What's halfway between 14 and 32?') a student might first estimate 22, but then checks their answer and finds that 22 is 8 away from 14, but 22 is 10 away from 32. So they move their answer up by one to get 23.

Add half the difference to the smaller number (probably the most common real strategy). The difference between 32 and 14 is 18. The answer is then 9 more than 14, which is 23.

Cut each number in half, and add the results together. The answer is then 7+16, which is 23.

Start at each number and count toward the middle simultaneously.

Start at some easy number in between, and then determine the average of the differences from that number and the two given numbers. Using the above example, we could choose 20, so the differences would be 6 and 12. Then find the average of these differences (which would be 9) and add that to the smaller number: 14 + 9 = 23.

Add the two numbers and divide by two, which is the standard average formula.

$$\frac{14 + 32}{2} = 23$$

Measurement

Review the material from the Class Three measurement main lesson. The metric system should be introduced with its common measures, and some teachers only cover weight and capacity in Class Four.

In Britain the metric system was introduced in the 1970s and the old imperial system was no longer taught in state schools. However, it can be briefly reviewed, as some elements of the imperial system are still used (like miles), and the United States uses measurements that are based on the imperial system (though their capacity measures are different). The Conti-

nent of Europe, the Irish Republic and most other English-speaking countries use the metric system. Teaching both systems also gives the students agility in maths.

Word problems

Simple written word problems are now introduced. Here are some examples of word problems to be done in Class Four:

- How can we divide £2292 evenly between six people? (This problem can be worked on in groups as part of an introduction to the full process for vertical division. See *A step-by-step progression for vertical (long) division,* pp. 91f)
- If we cut 8 apples into quarters, how many pieces do we have?
- If Mary's mother buys oranges for £4.50 and peaches for £3.10, how much does she have to pay? If she gives the cashier a £10 note, what should she get back for change? (Give many problems like this where the students need to determine how much change is given.)

Our puzzle and game book

Class Four can also be a great time to bring riddles and puzzle problems to the class. Randy Evans' book, *Fun with Puzzles, Games and More,* is intended as a resource for maths teachers in Classes Four through to Twelve, in part to supplement the normal classroom material. It provides ideas for that 'something different'.

Maths main lesson block 1: An introduction to fractions

New material and content

In this block, the students discover a new number world.

Language is an important part of understanding fractions. They become familiar with new words like numerator, denominator, mixed number, improper fraction, etc.

Our goal is to bring the students to a basic understanding of what a fraction is (e.g. what ⅝ really means).

Equivalent fractions. The students should clearly understand the idea of equivalent fractions (e.g. that ¾ is the same as ⁶⁄₈).

The students work primarily with proper fractions, but also become familiar with improper fractions and mixed numbers.

Don't forget to review and practise! Previously introduced material needs to be reviewed, practised, and furthered (see *Practice and review of old material*, p. 80).

Movement

The first week

Day 1. On the first day, we introduce fractions with food that is divided into pieces. We say clearly that you divide it first in half, then half again, and so on. That's it for the first day (the food can then be eaten)!

Day 2. On the second day of the block, we can 'move' the fraction from the first day. For example, if we divided a cake into 16 pieces on the first day, then we can 'walk it' on the second day. Every step represents a piece of the cake. The class then walks and speaks the fraction:

$\frac{1}{16}, \frac{2}{16}, \frac{3}{16}$ ... up to $\frac{15}{16}$ and $\frac{16}{16}$ (but we say 'one')

And then we do the whole thing backwards! While doing this, we make the students aware of how to properly pronounce the fractions. After this has been worked on, we can then do a new example of dividing something into pieces (e.g. dividing four apples into six pieces each).

Day 3. If we divided four apples into six pieces on the previous day, we can now walk by sixths until we reach 4.

$\frac{1}{6}, \frac{2}{6}, \frac{3}{6}, \frac{4}{6}, \frac{5}{6},$ 'One',

$1\frac{1}{6}, 1\frac{2}{6}, 1\frac{3}{6}, 1\frac{4}{6}, 1\frac{5}{6},$ 'Two',

$2\frac{1}{6}, 2\frac{2}{6}, 2\frac{3}{6}, 2\frac{4}{6}, 2\frac{5}{6},$ 'Three',

$3\frac{1}{6}, 3\frac{2}{6}, 3\frac{3}{6}, 3\frac{4}{6}, 3\frac{5}{6},$ 'Four'

And then we do it backwards! After this has been worked on, we can then do another new example of dividing something into pieces.

Days 4 and 5. We build very systematically on what we have done in the first three days.

The second week

During the second week, we give the class a fraction and they walk forwards (or backwards) to a certain number.

Example: We tell the class to start at $3\frac{3}{4}$ and step up to 6. Their steps are then:

$3\frac{3}{4}, 4, 4\frac{1}{4}, 4\frac{2}{4}, 4\frac{3}{4}, 5, 5\frac{1}{4}, 5\frac{2}{4}, 5\frac{3}{4}, 6$

Example: We tell the class to start at $3\frac{6}{8}$ and step up to 6. Their steps are then:

$$3\frac{6}{8},\ 3\frac{7}{8},\ 4,\ 4\frac{1}{8},\ 4\frac{2}{8},\ 4\frac{3}{8},\ 4\frac{4}{8},\ 4\frac{5}{8},\ 4\frac{6}{8},\ 4\frac{7}{8},\ 5,$$
$$5\frac{1}{8},\ 5\frac{2}{8},\ 5\frac{3}{8},\ 5\frac{4}{8},\ 5\frac{5}{8},\ 5\frac{6}{8},\ 5\frac{7}{8},\ 6.$$

Example: We tell the class to start at $1\frac{2}{6}$ and step down to zero. Their steps are then:

$$1\frac{2}{6},\ 1\frac{1}{6},\ 1,\ \frac{5}{6},\ \frac{4}{6},\ \frac{3}{6},\ \frac{2}{6},\ \frac{1}{6},\ 0.$$

The students should become more at ease with the fraction line; it becomes part of them.

The students should write down what they have practised into their practice books (e.g. they should write the same row of fraction steps from memory on the same day that they did it).

Working with manipulatives

Fractions with food. For the first week, we suggest starting the block with various edible objects (e.g. pies, pizza, pancakes, apples, chocolate) – preferably, each day, something of a different shape than the day before. For example, one day we work with pizza (circle), the next day apples (sphere), the next day a slice of bread (rectangle), the next day string cheese (line), and on the last day, a tall, round cake (which can be cut in many different ways).

Fractions with paper. It is best for the children to create their own manipulatives for fractions. After we have tasted our fractions, we can then cut fractions from various shapes on paper: circles, triangles, rectangles, and squares. Again, the students need to experience differ-

ent shapes for the same fraction. These paper fractions should be glued into their main lesson books.

Fraction envelopes. The children should also make extra sets of these paper fractions and keep them in an envelope. These 'fraction envelopes' will be used later to help with adding, subtracting and finding equivalent fractions.

Bookwork

The students should draw some of the 'food fractions' that were done in class.

They should include several examples with 'paper fractions' (the fractions should be written on the shapes).

One page should have different cuttings for each fraction.

The main lesson book should also include the key concepts, such as: numerator, denominator, mixed number, improper fraction, etc.

Visit *www.JamieYorkPress.com* to see full-colour pages from students' main lesson books.

Maths main lesson block 2: Adding and subtracting fractions

New material and content

Finding common denominators

This concept needs a good deal of practice! It is best for the children to have had a fair amount of practice with Least Common Multiples (LCM) before the start of this main lesson block.

Example: What is the common denominator for ⅚ and ¼? This is the same as asking:

'Where do the denominators meet? The students should then make a table, similar to this:

6	4
6	4
12	8
	12

These problems can be made visual by using the cutout pieces from their 'fraction envelopes' from main lesson block 1.

For more visual ideas, see John van de Walle's book, *Elementary and middle school mathematics*.

Adding & subtraction with unlike denominators
Once the students understand how to find common denominators between two fractions with unlike denominators, we can introduce adding and subtracting such fractions. Limit this to fairly simple proper fractions (but the answers may exceed 1).

Example: $\frac{5}{6} + \frac{1}{2}$

To do this, the students should work with the pieces in their fraction envelope. They take 5 pieces of ⅙ and 1 piece of ½ and see how they fit together. They should discover that ½ = ³⁄₆. Therefore, ⅚ + ½ is the same as ⅚ + ³⁄₆. The students can now easily see that together they make ⁸⁄₆, which can also be written as 1²⁄₆ or 1⅓.

Example: $\frac{3}{4} - \frac{1}{3}$

This could be the most difficult problem they do in this main lesson block. They should again use the pieces from their fraction envelope, as with the previous example. In this case, they would be working with 12 as the common denominator.

Vertical multiplication
In Class Three, we worked with single-digit multipliers. Now we can introduce 2-digit and 3-digit multipliers.

Be sure to read *A step-by-step progression for vertical multiplication,* p. 91.

Review and practice
Previously introduced material needs to be reviewed, practised, and furthered (see *Practice and review of old material,* p. 80).

Movement
In the first block, the class 'walked' fractions. Now we can walk different fractions at the same time.

Example: (Using ⅛, ¼, ½) The students line up next to each other. The ⅛ students take a small step for every count, while the ¼ students take a medium step (twice the size of the ⅛ students) with every other count, and the ½ students step (four times the size of the ⅛ students) with every four counts, starting at four-eighths. And they continue to move along in this manner.

Working with manipulatives
The students can use their fraction envelopes when necessary.

Bookwork

The new concepts of this block (adding and subtracting fractions with unlike denominators, and vertical multiplication with two and 3-digit multipliers) need to be thoroughly explained in the main lesson books. They should show the step-by-step processes. Use space, colour, and drawings. Be creative!

Visit *www.JamieYorkPress.com* to see full-colour pages from students' main lesson books.

Maths main lesson block 3: Multiplication and division of fractions

New material and content

Multiplication with fractions

The typical approach for multiplying fractions is to simply multiply the numerators and multiply the denominators. However, without any build-up or explanation, this becomes a blind trick. Instead, we should lead the students to discover this for themselves. It thus becomes a strategic trick.

In order for the students to truly understand fraction multiplication, we need to translate the mathematical concepts into spoken language. We should, of course, start with simple examples, such as: $\frac{1}{2} \times \frac{1}{2} = \frac{1}{4}$ which means, 'one half of one half equals one quarter.'

We should slowly build up to more complicated problems like:

$$\frac{2}{3} \times \frac{2}{5} = \frac{4}{15}$$

We need to find ways to make it visible – perhaps in a different way each day (see *www.JamieYorkPress.com/download/* to see full-colour drawings of this, under *Fourth Grade Sample Main Lesson Pages P2*).

After several days of translating and drawing, the students slowly come to understand the strategic trick for multiplying fractions: we have to multiply the two numerators together and multiply the two denominators together.

Division with fractions

Our goal, once again, is to lead the students to discovering the strategic trick for themselves.

As with fraction multiplication, we should introduce fraction division by translating the mathematical concepts into spoken language.

Here is a step-by-step progression:

$12 \div 6 = 2$

How many times does 6 fit into 12?

$12 \div 4 = 3$

How many times does 4 fit into 12?

$12 \div 3 = 4$

How many times does 3 fit into 12?

$12 \div 2 = 6$

How many times does 2 fit into 12?

$12 \div 1 = 12$

How many times does 1 fit into 12?

$12 \div \frac{1}{2} = 24$

How many times does $\frac{1}{2}$ fit into 12?

$12 \div \frac{1}{3} = 36$

How many times does $\frac{1}{3}$ fit into 12?

$\frac{1}{2} \div \frac{1}{4} = 2$

How many times does $\frac{1}{4}$ fit into $\frac{1}{2}$?

A Teacher's Source Book for Mathematics in Classes 1 to 5

In this way, the students should discover for themselves that the strategic trick is to multiply by the reciprocal of the second fraction. Even if this discovery is led by a few of the 'quicker' students in the class, it is valuable for the whole class to see that it comes from some process.

Don't forget to review and practise! Previously introduced material needs to be reviewed, practised, and furthered (see *Practice and review of old material,* p. 80).

Movement

The movement exercises for fractions slowly transform from the physical to lively imaginative thinking. Starting now, the students have to do the maths movement internally, instead of doing it physically. This progresses, until in middle school, it has become a lively, inner movement.

Working with manipulatives

The students can either cut and paste fractions, or draw them.

Bookwork

The students should draw the new concepts of fraction multiplication and fraction division into their main lesson books.

Visit *www.JamieYorkPress.com* to see full-colour pages from students' main lesson books.

More ideas for teaching Class Four maths

Be sure to reread the chapter, *Teaching Maths in Lower Classes,* p. 9 at the start of this book.

Arithmetic facts review sheets

You can download Class Four arithmetic facts review sheets free from *www.JamieYorkPress.com/downloads/* (and go to 4th Grade).

These maths fact sheets are intended as review of the Class Three arithmetic facts practice sheets. It is important that the students first do those Class Three practice sheets and are very familiar with the 105 facts (p. 77) before doing these Class Four review sheets.

Timing

Each sheet has 30 problems. There are 100 sheets in the whole set. A class should do three sheets per week (on average) throughout the year.

Caution! This should be fun and easy for the students. If successful, this builds their confidence. It is important to make sure that these sheets don't become torture for the students. Try to de-emphasise the importance of speed (this can wait until Class Five). Help the students realise that improvement is important.

A note regarding division with remainders

Towards the end of the Class Three arithmetic facts practice sheets, we introduced division with remainders. On those sheets, these remainder problems looked something like:

$$31 \div 5 = \underline{\quad} r \underline{\quad},$$

which warned the students that they were remainder problems. In contrast, the Class Four review sheets don't warn the students of the remainder problems. Therefore, the problem is simply given as $31 \div 5 = \underline{\quad}$, and the student should write the answer as 6 r 1. The students should know that on every sheet (of 30 problems) there is always one remainder problem. This makes it consistent, and perhaps fun for the students to find the mystery remainder problem.

What comes next?

The next set of practice sheets is Class Five arithmetic facts speed sheets. They are designed to increase the calculation speed of the students.

The whole picture

The 30 problems listed on a particular sheet are only a part of a day's maths practice, which should only take about 5 minutes of class time. It would be very unfortunate if daily maths practice consisted of nothing more than the 30 arithmetic facts practice problems that appear on these sheets.

The elements of maths practice

The following list shows some of the aspects to consider when planning maths practice for the day.

Arithmetic facts review sheet. The teacher copies by hand the 30 problems from a given day (that is, these Class Four arithmetic facts review sheets) onto paper to be photocopied* (about 5 minutes).

Mental arithmetic. The teacher may decide to read the first six problems out loud.

Extra maths practice problems. There should be a few problems that the teacher comes up with and writes on the board. The students copy them into their practice books and work out the answers. These problems also include practice and review of material covered in previous maths blocks. (This takes 20 to 25 minutes if the class is in a maths block, otherwise only 5 minutes.)

Challenge problems. It is important that the last few problems (that the teacher adds on) be more challenging in order to keep the 'quicker' students fully engaged.

And what happens if… ?

We hope that it won't happen, but even when most of the class is doing well with these sheets, there may be a few children who still haven't solidly learned their arithmetic facts. In order to help these children, it may be helpful to give them a multiplication/division table (i.e. a square for the tables). Additionally, these students could study the basic arithmetic problems with flashcards during morning practice time.

---

* Try to find ways to reduce the amount of paper being used. For example, rather than using one sheet of paper each day, each side could be divided into three columns (i.e. 6 days per sheet). This is one way to help develop an environmental consciousness in the students.

A Teacher's Source Book for Mathematics in Classes 1 to 5

Step-by-step progressions

Vertical multiplication (with 2-digit multipliers)

The students should draw columns for the place values: thousands, hundreds, tens, and ones. It may be that graphing paper (with square grids) is helpful for students.

We strongly recommend that students write a '0' (in all classes) instead of a blank for the placeholder. This better shows that we are actually multiplying with tens, hundreds, thousands, etc.

We recommend that the students work towards avoiding writing the small 'carry' number on top of the multiplication problem. Instead, they should simply keep it in their heads.

Step 1:

```
                47      → 40 + 7
             ×  36      → 30 + 6
 6 × 7  =       42
 6 ×40  =      240
30×  7  =      210
30×40   =    +1200
              1692
```

Step 2:

```
              2 4
               47
             × 36
47×  6  =      282
47×30   =    +1410
              1692
```

Step 3:

```
              2 4
               47
             × 36
               282
             +1410
              1692
```

Step 4 (without the carry digits):

```
               47
             × 36
               282
             +1410
              1692
```

Vertical (long) division

How to build up to an understanding of vertical division

The sequence of steps below works with the three-step division problem 2292 ÷ 6, which is probably too difficult of a starting point for the children. It would be better to start with a two-step problem, such as 152 ÷ 4.

This is only intended to give the teacher a sense of how to introduce vertical division in a way that builds up to an understanding of where the final procedure comes from.

Step 1 (as a story problem):

The whole class could use play money in small groups, and, in a practical manner, do what is shown here. This could be done with different numbers each day, for several days, before moving to the next stage. Nothing should be written down yet.

The gist of the story might look something like this:

Sally needs to divide £2292 evenly between 6 people. At first, she gives £200 to each person. This means she just gave away £1200, so she has (2292 – 1200) £1092 left. She then gives £150 more to each person, resulting in giving away (6 × 150) £900, and leaving her now with (1092 – 900) £192. Then she gives £20 to each person, which leaves her with (192 – 120) £72 dollars. Lastly, she gives away £12 to each person, which leaves her with nothing. Each person ends up with (200 + 150 + 20 + 12) £382. Therefore, we can say that 2292 ÷ 6 = 382.

Step 2 (accounting format):

The actions of the above problem can be written like this:

```
 Pot of money        Each person
    2292
   -1200    ← × 6  ← 200
    1092
   - 900    ← × 6  ← 150
    192
   - 120    ← × 6  ←  20
    72
   - 72     ← × 6  ← +12
     0         Total = 382
```

Step 3 (flexible vertical division):

This method looks similar to normal vertical division, but is flexible. Students can do it in many different ways to get the correct answer, as opposed to normal vertical division, which is rigid (for instance, the first digit must be a '3', etc.).

Flexible vertical division looks like this:

```
  200 + 150 + 20 + 12 = 382
 6 2292
  -1200
   1092
  - 900
    192
  - 120
     72
   - 72
      0
```

Step 4 (vertical division with zeros):

Now we can challenge the students to 'give away the money' in a way such that you have to give away the correct number of hundreds first, then the correct number of tens, and finally the correct number of ones. It looks like this:

```
   300 + 80 + 2 = 382
 6 2292
  -1800
    492
  - 480
     12
   - 12
      0
```

Step 5 ('normal' vertical division):

This is the usual way that vertical division is done. If the whole build up is done successfully, then students may be really excited about learning this as a shortcut for what they have already learned.

```
    382
 6 2292
  -18
   49
  -48
   12
  -12
    0
```

Class Five Maths

Overview of child development in Class Five

We leave the troubled lives of the Norse gods behind as the sun heralds a beautiful start of a new day. This is now the middle of the lower school years. In Class Five, temperaments and talents become more visible, and the student communicates easily between the inner and the outer world. There is an increased interest in social interactions. Breathing and blood circulation become harmonised. The proportions of the physical body are in harmony, thereby allowing for graceful physical movements. The children's cognitive capacities are increasing, which is accompanied by a desire to be challenged. They want to improve their work because they want to be proud of their work. They want and need constructive feedback.

The Class Five history curriculum, which starts with the ancient cultures and culminates in Greek history, develops their orientation in time. In language arts, the students are introduced to the verb tenses. In music, the class can now learn to sing multi-part harmonies.

The students have matured and now have an ability for a deeper understanding of more complex, mathematical concepts. This is the time to become confident in maths concepts from previous years (e.g. vertical division, multiplication, fractions, etc.). We give the students more challenging problems, which

slowly, with regular practice, help to increase their skill level. It is in Classes Five (and Six) that the students solidify their foundation in basic arithmetic. The new topic of decimal fractions sets the stage for the introduction to percentages in Class Six.

Curriculum summary for Class Five maths

Fractions
The students should become fluent when working with common and unlike denominators.

All four processes ($+, -, \times, \div$) with common fractions and mixed numbers should be practised regularly.

Decimal fractions are introduced. Place value practice supports this.

Measurement
The metric system is revised and expanded, which can be nicely integrated with decimal fractions.

A brief review of the imperial measurement system can be integrated into our work with the metric system.

Geometry
Freehand geometry. The students should create many beautiful drawings of circles, squares, triangles, angles, divisions of the circle, etc.,

all freehand, without the aid of ruler or compasses. The accuracy required with this takes great focus and will.

We can bring an imaginative picture of the Pythagorean theorem at this time.

We can also introduce perimeter and area.

The wonder of number
This can be a central theme for a creative main lesson. The idea is to bring several properties of numbers that will leave the students with a feeling of wonder.

There are many topics and mathematical properties that can accomplish this (for instance, square and triangular numbers, powers of two, divisibility rules, perfect numbers, sum and difference theorems, etc.). See details under *Maths main lesson block 3*, p. 100.)

Review and practice
Consolidation of skills that were introduced in earlier years is a major theme for both Class Five and Class Six maths. Systematic review and practice is needed throughout the year.

It is especially important to review (and further) all work with vertical arithmetic (addition, subtraction, long multiplication, and long division), and all work with fractions.

Arithmetic facts
Review and practice of the arithmetic facts is still important. This can be done as part of daily oral mental arithmetic, and further reinforced a few times per week with arithmetic fact practice sheets (e.g. our Class Five arithmetic facts speed sheets).

Also, work with challenging multiplication facts (from 13 to 25 times tables) can be done, which may have been started in Class Four.

Recommended reading
Henning Anderson, *Active Arithmetic.*
Herman von Baravalle, *The Teaching of Arithmetic and the Waldorf School Plan.*
Julia Diggins, *String, Straight Edge and Shadow.*
Dorothy Harrer, *Maths Lessons for Elementary Grades.*
Christoph Jaffke, *Rhythms, Rhymes, Games and Songs for the Lower School.*
Lipping Ma, *Knowing and Teaching Elementary Mathematics.*
Ernst Schuberth, *Geometry Lessons in the Waldorf School*, Vol. 2. This is an excellent book, but, for the most part, what he has listed for Class Four, we would recommend for Class Five, and what he has listed for Class Five, such as work with a compass and straight edge, we would recommend for Class Six.
Heather Thomas, *A Journey Through Time.*
John A. van de Walle, *Elementary and Middle School Mathematics.*
Ron Jarman, *Teaching Mathematics in Rudolf Steiner Schools for Classes I–VIII.* We recommend this book for ideas for Class Four and up.
Malba Tahan, *The Man Who Counted.*
Publication details: *Suggested Reading*, p. 125.

Lessons and topics for Class Five maths

Scheduling

The curriculum calls again for twelve weeks of maths (three main lesson blocks of four weeks each), with one week of review at the end of the school year.

Don't forget!!
- Every day, we should *review* the previous day's lesson.
- Every day, we should bring *something new* to the children.
- Every day, the students should *practise* the new material and selected review topics.

Practice and review (of old material)

Consolidation of skills that were introduced in earlier years is a major theme for both Class Five and Class Six maths. Systematic review and practice is needed throughout the year.

Rudolf Steiner recommended one practice lesson per week for maths, beginning in Class Five.

During each maths main lesson, we should be sure to practise the material from previous blocks and previous classes for at least half an hour every day.

Most of the topics listed were introduced some time ago. In order for the children to learn a topic well, it needs to be systematically reviewed. Obviously, all previous topics cannot be reviewed every day. The teacher needs to decide which topics are the most important. Some of these topics may need to be reviewed and practised nearly every day, whether the class is in a maths block, or not. As a general guideline, the class should practise 30 minutes daily, when in a maths block, and about 10 minutes daily (in the morning) when not in a maths block. (Also see *Review and practice* under *Principles of Waldorf education,* p. 15.)

Working vertically with the four processes
Every day we should practise some problems using vertical addition, subtraction, multiplication, and division. We can also integrate work with decimals into this, as well as problems with extra zeros at the end.

Vertical addition and subtraction. Continued from what was done in Class Four, but now with larger numbers. Regular practice is needed.

Vertical multiplication. Simply continue and further what was done in Class Four. Perhaps now we can even multiply two 4-digit numbers together. Regular practice is needed.

Vertical (long) division. Last year, in Class Four, vertical division was limited to single digit divisors. This year, we can work with 2-digit divisors (e.g. $1909 \div 23$), building up to problems like $63{,}206 \div 65$. Be sure to (at least occasionally) check answers to division problems by multiplying (with $1909 \div 23 = 83$, we should multiply 83×23 to make sure that it's equal to 1909).

Fractions

All four processes with the common fractions and mixed numbers need to be thoroughly practised. Our work with fractions, which was begun last year, needs a good amount of attention. The students need to feel confident with fractions.

Addition and subtraction. The students should become fluent in working with common denominators and at ease with unlike denominators.

Multiplying and dividing common fractions should be thoroughly practised.

Mixed numbers should be worked with regularly, including all four processes.

Estimating

The students should learn to estimate before calculating a problem.

Arithmetic facts

Speed sheets. Even if the class successfully learned all of their arithmetic facts in Class Three and Four, practising these facts in Class Five is still important. This can be done as part of daily oral mental arithmetic, and further reinforced a few times per week with arithmetic fact practice sheets.

Challenging multiplication facts. Previously, we had suggested that the Class Four teacher could select some new multiplication facts from the 13 through to the 25 times tables. Some of these can be done by the whole class, and some can be given just to those students needing an extra challenge. This work may be continued in Class Five (and Six).

Mental arithmetic

Practise mental arithmetic daily (for 10 minutes or less).

Work up to calculations like: $84 - 26$; $423 - 60$; $546 + 76$; 40×600; 5378×100; $24,000 \div 600$.

Halfway problems. We can continue doing problems that were done in earlier classes (like, 'What is halfway between 26 and 56?'), but now we can add problems that work with fractions, like:

- What number is halfway between $\frac{3}{8}$ and $\frac{7}{8}$?
- What number is halfway between $\frac{3}{7}$ and $\frac{4}{7}$?
- What is halfway between 25.5 and 26.3?

Word problems

Word problems given in Class Five should be more practical, such as:

- If a kilogram of cheese is divided evenly between 8 people, then how much does each person get?
- There are 23 Class Five students working on a garden project. Each one works $1\frac{1}{2}$ hours. How many working-hours is that altogether?

Simple *unit cost* problems, including:

- If oranges cost £1.32 per kilograms, then how much do you need to pay for 5 kilograms of oranges?

- If 4 kilograms of oranges cost £5.16, then what is the price per kilogram?
- If 4 kilograms of oranges cost £5.16, how much do 7 kilograms of oranges cost?
- If 4.3 kilograms of oranges cost £5.16, then what is the price per kilogram?
- If 4.3 kilograms of oranges cost £5.16, then how much do 7 kilograms of oranges cost?

Puzzles

Class Five is a good time to give puzzles, but be careful to select a puzzle that is at the appropriate level. Puzzles that are too hard can be discouraging for many of the students. The right puzzle can bring joy into the classroom for all of the students.

Randy Evans' book, *Fun with Puzzles, Games and More,* is intended as a resource for maths teachers in Classes Four through to Twelve, in part to supplement the normal classroom material. It provides ideas for that 'something different'.

Maths magic trick. Here is an example from the puzzle and game book: Start with two numbers between 1 and 9. Add these two numbers together to get a third number. Add the second and third number together to get a fourth number. Add the third and fourth numbers together to get a fifth number. Continue this process until you have ten numbers. Add together all ten numbers. Divide by 11. This final answer will always be equal to the seventh number in your list.

Maths main lesson block 1: Decimal fractions

New material and content

Decimal fractions

We can begin with the question: what is the meaning of 'deca'? Some examples: *deca*gon, *deca*de, *Dec*ember (the tenth month of the Roman calendar).

We should review our place value work in Class Two and Three. At that time, each step in place value (moving to the left) increased the value by a multiple of ten of that place. Now, with decimal fractions, each step taken to the right decreases the value of the place by a factor of ten.

A fun exercise with decimals

There is a hat for each place value (e.g. thousands, hundreds, tens, ones, tenths, hundredths, thousandths). One student is the decimal point. Starting out simply, we could just work with three digits. So we line up three students and give each one a digit – for example, the leftmost student gets a 7, the next student gets a 1, and the last student gets a 5.

The 'decimal' student then positions himself between two of the digits – assume for now between the 7 and the 1. Another student then takes the collection of hats, and gives the 'ones' hat to the student holding the 7, the 'tenths' hat to the student holding the 1, and the 'hundredths' hat to the student holding the 5. The class then reads it as 'seven and fifteen hundredths'.

We can then collect just the hats, and ask what happens if the decimal place moves one place to the left or right. The hats then get reassigned and the class reads the new number.

Speech and language
Throughout Class Five, we should always say 'decimal fractions' instead of just 'decimals'. We should also speak these numbers in a way that shows they are fractions. For example, with 1.42, try to avoid saying 'one point four two', but rather say, 'one and forty-two hundredths'. This may be phased out in Class Six or Class Seven.

Fluency and practice
The students should quickly become comfortable with decimal fractions.

We can say to the students, 'Make this number 10 times bigger, or 100 times smaller, etc.'

The students need to be at ease when there are several digits behind the decimal point and be able to answer questions like: 'What is bigger 1.78 or 1.769 93?'

We should also practise rounding decimals.

We should show the students how most monetary systems are based on the decimal system.

We can bring decimal fractions of a second in relation to sporting achievements.

The four processes with decimal fractions
The four processes with decimal fractions should also be introduced.

For vertical addition and subtraction of decimal fractions, place value is very important.

Therefore, we need to make sure that we line up the decimal point.

We should also practise the four processes with decimal fractions orally (mental arithmetic) and in written horizontal form as well (e.g. £3.25 × 10 = ___).

Simple equivalences
The students should discover that, for decimal fractions, we need to find equivalent fractions in tenths, hundredths, and thousandths. Examples are:

One half = $\frac{1}{2}$ = $\frac{5}{10}$ = 0.5;
0.25 = $\frac{25}{100}$ = $\frac{1}{4}$, etc.

Practice of converting common fractions to decimal fractions is saved for the next maths block.

Don't forget to review and practise
Material that has been introduced in previous blocks and in previous years needs to be reviewed, practised, and furthered – 30 minutes per day during a maths main lesson. (See *Practice and review of old material* under *Lessons and topics for Class Five maths*, p. 95)

Movement and manipulatives
There are many exercises that the teacher can create (see also *A fun exercise with decimals*, p. 97).

Bookwork
Visit *www.JamieYorkPress.com* to see full-colour pages from students' main lesson books.

Maths main lesson block 2: Expanding the metric system

New material and content

This is the time when the understanding of the metric system can be expanded and brought into relation with decimal fractions.

Using both the imperial and metric systems, the students should measure a great many objects (and estimate each time before measuring). Only limited practice of conversion between imperial and metric should be done, perhaps restricted to those measure most often shown in imperial (like miles to kilometres).

Linear Measurement

In order to make it practical, we can begin, as we did in Class Three, with measuring things in the classroom. We can measure students' heights, the perimeter of books, the lengths of desks, the blackboard, and the whole classroom. We can even measure the school grounds. We can use rulers, metre sticks, or tape measures. We should measure both in metres and in centimetres.

Always estimate before measuring!

From all of our measuring work, we can then introduce the less commonly used units of linear measurement: decimetre (dm), decametre (dam) and hectometre (hm). The students need to get a sense that, interspersed with the familiar measurements of millimetre, centimetre, metre and kilometre, every step is a factor of ten.

The students should practise simple conversions from one unit to the other within the metric system. (e.g. 7 m = ___ cm). Keep it simple. Much more of this should be practised in the coming years.

Weight

The students should weigh many objects both briefly in the imperial system, and mainly in the metric system. Once again, it should be practical, and always remember to estimate before weighing.

In the imperial system ounces, pounds, (and perhaps stones and hundredweight). In the metric system the less commonly used units – centigram (cg), decigram (dg), decagram (dag), hectogram (hg) – can be added to familiar milligram (mg), gram (g) kilogram (kg) and tonne.* Again, every step is a factor of ten.

The students should practise converting from one unit to the other within one system (e.g. 18 kg = ___ g, or 3 lb = ___ oz).

Capacity (volume)

Once again, the students find the capacity of many objects (e.g. bottles, cans, tins, etc.)using a calibrated jug, briefly in the imperial system and then in the metric system. Again, it should be practical, and always remember to estimate before measuring.

In the imperial system use fluid ounce, pint and gallon. In the metric system again the less

---

* The metric tonne of 1000 kg is roughly the same as an imperial ton of 2240 lb ($\approx$ 1016 kg).

commonly used units – centilitre (cℓ), decilitre (dℓ), decalitre (daℓ), hectolitre (hℓ), kilolitre (kℓ) – can be added to the millilitre (mℓ) and litre (ℓ).

Don't forget to review and practise – 30 minutes per day during a maths main lesson! Material that has been introduced in previous blocks and in previous years needs to be reviewed, practised, and furthered (see *Practice and review of old material* under *Lessons and topics for Class Five maths,* p. 95).

The material from the first block on decimal fractions needs to be reviewed and practised. The students can now learn to convert from common fractions to decimal fractions, and vice versa.

Movement and manipulatives

Through all of the hands-on work, there is much movement.

Walking (or running) various distances is also a good idea (for instance, get the whole class to walk a distance of one kilometre away from the school).

Bookwork

The students should make charts, tables, and graphs of measurements (estimates and actual). As always, the illustrations should be done beautifully.

Visit *www.JamieYorkPress.com* to see full-colour pages from students' main lesson books.

Maths main lesson block 3: Freehand geometry and the wonder of number

New material and content
Timing and balance

Given that there are two separate topics covered in this main lesson, it is important that we balance how much is done during any one day, and during the entire main lesson block. We recommend that an equal amount of time is spent on the three areas of geometry, wonder of number and maths practice/review.

Freehand geometry

Most of the drawings with this topic involve circles, rectangles, angles and triangles, all with a good amount of variations.

After form drawing in the lower classes, we step right into freehand geometry in Class Five. These geometrical drawings require extra care because they are so ordered. The drawings demand will forces from the students as they learn to follow the geometrical laws of the forms.

Freehand geometry also develops the feeling capacity for the ideal form itself. The connection with the archetypal forms has to come from the feeling level, and not yet out of the intellectual realm.

The students should draw the forms accurately with lead pencil. Certain aspects of the form can be accentuated with colour pencils and shadings; beauty and exactness are important. However, any artwork or shading should be simple, with the purpose of bringing out the most important characteristics of the form.

Some of the drawings can be done on larger pieces of paper.

The use of the geometric tools (compasses and straightedge) should wait until Class Six during the geometric drawing main lesson.

There are many wonderful ideas for freehand geometry in Ernst Schuberth's book, *Geometry Lessons in the Waldorf School,* Vol. 2. However, we recommend freehand geometry in Class Five, and geometric drawing (with compasses and straightedge) for Class Six, whereas Schuberth lists both of these a year earlier.

Area and perimeter of rectangles and squares can now be introduced.

Pythagorean theorem

Since ancient Greek history and culture is a theme of Class Five, we can tell Pythagoras' biography and introduce his theorem (see Julia Diggins' book, *String, Straight Edge and Shadow,* pp. 92–105).

By giving an artistic introduction to the Pythagorean theorem in Class Five, we are planting a seed for geometry in the upper classes. Connection with will and feeling is important. Be sure not to make it too intellectual.

The Pythagorean theorem is an important mathematical law. The children's first experience with it should be artistic and very hands-on. We are simply playing with the theorem; the intellectual concept is not yet introduced (see the sample drawing of this on our website).

The wonder of number

There are many ideas given overleaf (under *More ideas for teaching Class Five maths,* pp. 102f) for what could be brought to the class during this main lesson. Some of the possible topics are:

- Square and triangular numbers
- Powers of two
- Divisibility rules
- Perfect numbers
- Sum and difference theorems

These are all just ideas. None of it is compulsory. Whatever isn't covered in Class Five can be covered at any point in Classes Six to Eight, or not covered at all.

This is a truly wonderful main lesson to bring to the children as long as the teacher has the time and desire to learn and penetrate the material sufficiently. The teacher needs to find an appropriate and creative way to bring it to the children.

It is important that the students discover for themselves the properties of numbers described, or, at least that they acquire some understanding of where they come from. We should not just give the numbers and properties to them. Wonder arises from discovery!

Don't forget to review and practise – 30 minutes per day during a maths main lesson! Material that has been introduced in previous blocks and in previous years needs to be reviewed, practised, and furthered (see *Practice and review of old material,* p. 95).

Movement and manipulatives

The Pythagorean theorem can be cut out and glued (colour drawings of this are on *www.JamieYorkPress.com*).

Many movement exercises can be done outside, for example:

- The students can move their arms to represent different angles.
- The class can form a circle with one student at the centre and everyone else an equal distance from the centre person.
- In a similar way, the class can form different triangles, angles, squares, parallel lines, etc.

Making a right angle with a rope

The following is an example of how the Egyptians were able to make a right angle by using a rope.

Bring the class into a field and have a rope that is 36 metres long, with a knot tied 15 metres from one end and 12 metres from the other end. (The distance between the two knots should now be 9 metres.) Form a triangle with the rope, such that the three corners of the triangle are the two knots and the place where the ends of the rope come together. All three sides of the triangle should be tight and straight. The result should be a right triangle.

You should show that if one knot is moved a few feet, then you no longer get a right angle.

Bookwork

After practicing each geometric form on loose drawing paper, each form should be drawn beautifully in the main lesson book.

Visit *www.JamieYorkPress.com* to see full-colour pages from students' main lesson books.

More ideas for teaching Class Five maths

Wonder of number

Be sure to reread the chapter, *Teaching Maths in Lower Classes*, on p. 9 at the start of this book.

This entire section is intended for the wonder of number main lesson block. None of it is compulsory. Whatever isn't covered in Class Five, could be covered at any point in Classes Six to Eight, or not covered at all. A good amount of what is listed here is for the teacher's curiosity and interest. It should only be brought into the classroom if the teacher has adequately penetrated the material, and can find an appropriate and creative way to bring it to the children.

Square and triangular numbers

See Appendix, *Square and triangular numbers*, pp. 113f, for a listing of the square and triangular numbers.

Square numbers

The square numbers are 1, 4, 9, 16, etc. They are found by squaring each whole number: 1^2, 2^2, 3^2, 4^2, etc.

They can be geometrically made into squares by placing dots into square shapes: three rows of three make 9, four rows of four make 16, etc., as shown opposite.

Alternatively, they can also be found by adding sequences of odd numbers. For example, the fourth square number can be found by adding the first four odd numbers: 1 + 3 + 5 + 7, which is 16. Similarly, the sixth square number can be found by adding the first six odd numbers: 1 + 3 + 5 + 7 + 9 + 11, which is 36.

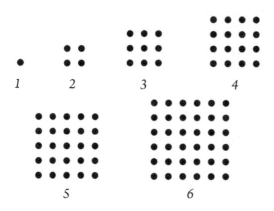

Triangular numbers

The triangular numbers are 1, 3, 6, 10, 15, 21, 28, 36, etc. The reason that they are called triangular can be seen by looking at the way that the dots are placed in a triangular form, as shown below.

The triangular numbers can be found by adding a sequence of numbers. For example, the fourth triangular number is found by adding the first four numbers: 1 + 2 + 3 + 4, which is 10. Similarly, the sixth triangular number is found by adding 1 + 2 + 3 + 4 + 5 + 6, which is 21.

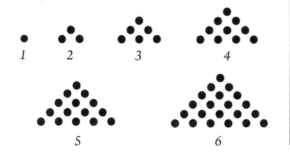

A neat theorem

The sum of two consecutive triangular numbers is a square number. A nice 'proof' of this is shown with the drawing here. This can be quite a thrill for students to discover on their own!

Have the students try to find the first three numbers that are both square and triangular. There are only seven numbers below 2 billion that are both square and triangular. They are 1, 36, 1225, 41,616, 1,413,721, 48,024,900 and 1,631,432,881

Powers of two

See *Powers of two table* in the Appendix, pp. 116f.

We can ask the children: What do we get if we multiply two 2s together? How about multiplying three 2s together? And ten 2s? And twenty 2s? They may be surprised how the results get large very quickly.

It may be best to not introduce notation that uses exponents until Class Six.

Divisibility rules

A number is evenly divisible by **10** (that is, can be divided by 10 with no remainder) only if the number ends in a 0.

A number is evenly divisible by **5** only if the number ends in a 5 or a 0.

A number is evenly divisible by **2** only if it is even.

A number is evenly divisible by **4** only if the last two digits are divisible by 4. This is particularly fun for the children because someone can give them any large number and they only have to listen for the last two digits in order to determine if the number is evenly divisible by 4.

The students can then try to figure out how to do this quickly in the case that the last two digits are greater than 50. One method is to subtract 20, 40, 60 or 80 in order to make it easier.

Example: Is 6,380,716 evenly divisible by 4?

We see that it ends in 16, which is evenly divisible by 4. Therefore, 6,380,716 is also evenly divisible by 4.

Example: Is 98,273,474 evenly divisible by 4?

We see that it ends in 74. We subtract 60, leaving us with 14, which isn't evenly divisible by 4. Therefore, 98,273,474 is not evenly divisible by 4.

A number is evenly divisible by **3** only if the sum of the digits is divisible by 3. For example, for 71,284 we add up the digits to get 22. Because 22 is not divisible by 3, we can conclude that 71,284 is not evenly divisible by 3.

A number is evenly divisible by **9** only if the sum of the digits is divisible by 9.

Perfect, abundant, and deficient numbers

See *Perfect, abundant, and deficient numbers* in the Appendix, pp. 114f, for a listing.

The Greeks (especially the Pythagoreans) believed that certain numbers had special meaning and significance. They studied perfect, abundant, and deficient numbers in detail.

What are perfect, abundant, and deficient numbers? In general, a whole number is categorised by the sum of its factors. In order to determine whether a given whole number is perfect, abundant or deficient, we first list all the number's factors, except for the number itself. Then we sum up the numbers in that list.

If this sum is *equal* to the number itself, then we say that the number is *perfect*.

If this sum is *less than* the number itself, then we say that the number is *deficient*.

If the sum is *greater than* the number itself, then we say that the number is *abundant*.

Discovering perfect numbers

Show the students that 10 is a deficient number because the sum of its factors (1, 2, 5) is less than 10. Then show the students that 20 is an abundant number because the sum of its factors (1, 2, 4, 5, 10) is greater than 20. Then tell the students that there are only two perfect numbers under 100, and let them try to find these two special numbers. (They are 6 and 28.)

More perfect numbers

Perfect numbers are extremely rare; there are only four perfect numbers below 10,000,000. The students now know that the first two perfect numbers are 6 and 28, and that the next perfect number is greater than 100. You can then mention that the third perfect number is less than 1000, and the fourth one is less than 10,000. Tell them that they will have to wait until Class

Seven to learn how to calculate these perfect numbers. (A bit of anticipation never hurts!)

Abundance quotient
The abundance quotient is the quotient that results when the sum of factors (without the number itself) is divided by the number itself.

Example: Determine whether the number 10 is perfect, abundant or deficient, and calculate its abundance quotient.

The list of factors for 10 is 1, 2, 5. The sum of these factors is 8, which is less than the number itself (10), so the number is deficient. The abundance quotient is 8 ÷ 10, which is 0.8.

Example: Determine whether the number 20 is perfect, abundant or deficient, and calculate its abundance quotient.

The list of factors for 20 is 1, 2, 4, 5, 10. The sum of these factors is 22, which is greater than the number itself (20), so the number is abundant. The abundance quotient is 22 ÷ 20, which is 1.1.

Example: Determine whether the number 28 is perfect, abundant or deficient, and calculate its abundance quotient.

The list of factors for 28 is 1, 2, 4, 7, 14. The sum of these factors is 28, which is equal to the number itself (28), so the number is perfect. The abundance quotient (for all perfect numbers) is exactly 1.

More about perfect, abundant, and deficient numbers (for the teacher)
There are 21 even abundant numbers under 100. The first odd abundant number is 945.

The first 7 perfect numbers are:* 6; 28; 496; 8128; 33,550,336; 8,589,869,056; 137,438,691,328.

Early on, the Greeks knew that the first three perfect numbers were 6, 28, and 496. They had troubles finding perfect numbers beyond that because the numbers were getting too large to list and add all the factors. They wanted to find an easier method for determining perfect numbers.

Euclid discovered a formula for calculating even perfect numbers around 300 BC. This formula made it possible to discover the next few perfect numbers, perhaps up to the seventh one (see *A Teacher's Source Book for Mathematics in Classes 6–8*, under Class Seven algebra, p. 96). In the 1600s, Jean Prestet found the eighth perfect number: 2,305,843,008,139,952,128.

There are no known odd perfect numbers, and it is one of the great mysteries of mathematics whether or not an odd perfect number could possibly exist.

Sum and difference theorems
Each of the theorems overleaf expresses some surprising law about the relationship of numbers. If properly brought to the children, this can engender a real sense of wonder. It should only be brought to the children if the teacher has developed a good connection to this material.

---

* Note that '1' is not considered to be a perfect number for the same reason that it isn't considered to be a prime number: it is the basis of all numbers. Also, our list of factors does not include the number itself, so the number 1 doesn't have any numbers in its list of factors.

The challenge is to not make it too abstract. Try to make it playful.

The Greeks were very interested in how numbers could be expressed as the sum or difference of other special numbers (e.g. prime numbers or square numbers). It was the famous French mathematician, Pierre de Fermat, who, around 1640, came up with the theorems below (except for the first one).

Goldbach's conjecture
Every even number can be expressed as the sum of two prime numbers.

Simply ask the children how many ways they can find to express 90 as the sum of two prime numbers. Have them list the different possibilities that they have found on the board. They will be amazed to see that there are nine ways to express 90 as the sum of two primes $(7+83; 11+79; 17+73; 19+71; 23+67; 29+61; 31+59; 37+53; 43+47)$.

In contrast, there are only two ways to express 68 as the sum of two primes $(7+61$ and $31+37)$.

Once we get past the first few even numbers, almost all of them can be expressed as the sum of two prime numbers in multiple ways, yet the number of possible ways varies greatly.

While most mathematicians believe that this theorem is true, nobody has been able to prove it (but many have tried!).

See *Even numbers as the sum of two primes,* p. 119 in the Appendix for a list of all the ways that the even numbers from 4 to 150 can be expressed as the sum of two primes.

The difference of two square numbers
Every prime number, except for 2, can be expressed as the difference of two square numbers in one and only one way.

The students should first make a list of consecutive square numbers, and see how the differences/distances grow:

$$1 \quad 4 \quad 9 \quad 16 \quad 25 \quad 36$$
$$3 \quad 5 \quad 7 \quad 9 \quad 11 \quad \text{... (differences)}$$

Given that the above differences between neighbours form the list of odd numbers, we can easily see how any odd number can be expressed as the difference of two squares. For example, we can express 7 as $16 - 9$ (which is $4^2 - 3^2$). Similarly, we can express 15 as $64 - 49$ (which is $8^2 - 7^2$).

The real surprise with the above theorem is that it says, if the odd number is a prime number, then it can be expressed as a difference of two squares in only one way. For example, 15 can be expressed as the difference of two squares in two ways: either as $8^2 - 7^2$ or as $4^2 - 1^2$. This does not contradict our theorem because 15 is not a prime number. On the other hand, 7 is prime, so we know that it can only be expressed as $4^2 - 3^2$.

See *Odd numbers as the difference of two squares,* p. 121 in the Appendix for a list of all the ways that the odd numbers from 3 to 299 can be expressed as the difference of two squares.

The sum of two square numbers
If a number is prime and has a remainder of 1 after dividing it by 4, then it can be expressed as

the sum of two square numbers in one and only one way.

The number 73 is both prime and has a remainder of 1 when divided by 4. This theorem tells us that there must be exactly one way to express 73 as the sum of two squares. In the Appendix there is a list of all the ways that the numbers from 2 to 442 can be expressed as the sum of two squares (*Numbers as the sum of two squares*, p. 122). Looking at this list, we see that 73 can be expressed only as $8^2 + 3^2$.

If a number is prime and has a remainder of 3 after dividing it by 4, then it is not possible to express it as a sum of two square numbers.

The number 43 is both prime and has a remainder of 3 when divided by 4. The theorem says that it must be impossible to express 43 as the sum of two squares. Looking at the list in the Appendix confirms that 43 can't be expressed as the sum of two squares.

If a number is not prime, then there are a variety of possibilities – it may be that the number can be expressed as the sum of two square numbers in one way, in multiple ways, or not at all.

Looking at the list in the Appendix, we can see the following:

45 can be expressed as the sum of two squares in exactly one way: $6^2 + 3^2$.

48 cannot be expressed as the sum of two squares in any way.

50 is the first number that can be expressed as the sum of two squares in two ways: $5^2 + 5^2$ or $7^2 + 1^2$.

325 is the first number that can be expressed as the sum of two squares in three ways: $1^2 + 18^2$; $6^2 + 17^2$; $10^2 + 15^2$.

1105 is the first number that can be expressed as the sum of two squares in four ways: $4^2 + 33^2$; $9^2 + 32^2$; $12^2 + 31^2$; $23^2 + 24^2$.

Fermat's little theorem

Let x be equal to 2. Choose any number (but don't make it too big!), and call it Q. Calculate x^Q (which will need to be explained to the children without using exponent notation). Take this result and subtract x from it – the result we will call D. Here is the question: Is D evenly divisible by Q? The children should then try a variety of possible values for Q, from $Q = 2$ all the way up to $Q = 15$. What patterns do we notice?

Ultimately, we want to answer this question: 'By just looking at the value of Q, how can we predict whether D will be evenly divisible by Q?' The answer is Fermat's little theorem:

If Q is a prime number, then D will always be evenly divisible by Q.

And x can also be anything other than 2.*

---

* It would also seem that if Q is composite (i.e. not prime) then D won't be evenly divisible by Q. If $x = 2$, all of the composite numbers that we could reasonably try would support this statement. But, quite surprisingly, if we let $Q = 341$ (which is evenly divisible by 11), then the resulting 103-digit value for D turns out to be evenly divisible by 341. If x is greater than 2, then generally we can easily find composite values for Q that divide evenly into D.

Appendix

A maths curriculum summary for Classes One to Five

Class One
The world of numbers
Roman numerals. Begin with the Roman numerals, and then move into the (standard) Arabic numbers.

Quality of numbers. What is the quality of the numbers in the surrounding world?

Counting. Counting forward and backward to 100, with ease. Awaken a sense for number.

Number dictations. There should be number dictations starting in the second maths block.

Developing a sense of numbers
Rhythmical counting. Rhythmical counting serves as preparation for learning the times tables later.

Movement. The challenge is to synchronise the movement with the speaking voice.

Estimating. 'How many steps am I from the board?'

Beginning calculations
Introducing the four processes. The children become at ease with adding and subtracting numbers up to 24, and fluently up to 10.

Regrouping numbers. For example, how can we regroup the number ten?

Learning the 'easy' addition facts. All addition facts up to 10, as well as all of the doubles (e.g. 6 + 6, 7 + 7, 8 + 8, 9 + 9) should be learned by heart by the end of Class One.

Class Two
The world of numbers
The students should become at ease with the number world up to 1000 (and beyond?).

Estimating. We build up from the estimating done in Class One and progress to more challenging estimations.

Place value. Place value should be introduced and practised. This is an important step.

Addition and subtraction facts
By the end of the year, the class should learn by heart their addition facts (up to 24) and the corresponding subtraction facts. They should also be at ease with addition and subtraction up to 100.

The times/division tables
By the end of the year, the class should be comfortable with all of the times and division tables from 1 to 12, in a row. This requires daily, systematic work!

The four processes
Addition. By the end of the year, the class should be at ease with adding any 2-digit number with a 1-digit number (e.g. 57 + 6).

Subtraction. By the end of the year, the class should be at ease with subtracting any 1-digit number from a 2-digit number (e.g. 52 – 6), and also with subtracting two 2-digit numbers such that the answer is a 1-digit number (e.g. 72 – 69).

The students must gain an understanding of the concept of *multiplication and division,* such as: $3 \times 2 = 6$ means 'three groups of two make six'. $12 \div 3 = 4$ means 'how many groups of three fit in twelve?'

By the end of the year, the children should be able to do all four processes (even alternating on the same page) and know the difference between the processes without help. But keep the problems simple!

Time orientation
The days of the week and the months of the year.

The wonder of number
Geometrical patterns that arise from the times/division tables and the circle.

Class Three
The world of numbers
Fluent up to 1000 and at ease with the numbers up into the millions.

Learning all of the arithmetic facts
Now is the time to learn the multiplication and division facts (that come from these tables) out of order, as well as all of the addition facts and subtraction facts. Systematic daily work, both orally and written (e.g. with our arithmetic fact practice sheets) is needed.

The four processes: working vertically
An introduction to vertical addition ('carrying') and vertical subtraction ('borrowing'). Build up to adding two 4-digit numbers (like $8364 + 8375$) and subtracting two 3-digit numbers (like $643 – 387$).

An introduction to vertical multiplication. Only do single-digit multipliers (like 2347×5).

An introduction to vertical (long) division should wait until Class Four.

The four processes: working horizontally
Even though the children are being introduced to working with the four processes in vertical form, the bulk of their work with the four processes is still in horizontal form.

Measurement
Introduction to time, distance, weight, and volume, beginning with 'human measures' like cubit and foot, and then imperial measures.

Class Four
The world of numbers
Greatest common factor (GCF) and least common multiple (LCM).

The arithmetic facts
Continued work both orally and written (e.g. with our arithmetic fact review sheets).

The four processes
Regular practice is needed.

Horizontal addition and subtraction with problems like: $125 + 126, 895 + 112, 974 – 875$.

Vertical addition and subtraction. Work with larger numbers than what was done in Class Three.

Vertical multiplication. We can build up to 3-digit multipliers (e.g. 4372×836).

Vertical (long) division should be introduced. Build up to four-step problems. The divisors should be kept between 1 and 12 (e.g. $15,288 \div 6 = 2548$).

Fractions
An introduction to fractions, including: types of fractions, equivalent fractions, and simple arithmetic with fractions. The goal is to get to the end of Class Four with the class having a good understanding of the basics of fractions, and having the children saying, 'I like fractions!'

Measurement
Review Class Three measurement. If not already done in Class Three, introduce the metric system (distance, weight, and capacity). Begin doing simple conversion problems within each system.

Class Five
Fractions
The students should become fluent in working with common denominators and at ease with unlike denominators. Multiplying and dividing of common fractions should be thoroughly practised.

Decimal fractions
The number world of decimal fractions is introduced.

Measurement
Review the metric system, introducing less common measures. Some work on the imperial system can be integrated into our work with the metric system.

Geometry
Freehand geometry. The students create many beautiful drawings of circles, squares, triangles, angles, divisions of the circle, etc., all freehand, without the aid of a ruler or compasses.

We can bring an imaginative picture of the Pythagorean theorem.

We can also introduce perimeter and area.

The wonder of number
Some of the possible topics are: square and triangular numbers, powers of two, divisibility rules, perfect numbers, and sum and difference theorems. Leave them in wonder!

Review and practice
It is especially important to review (and further) all work with vertical arithmetic (addition, subtraction, long multiplication, and long division), and all work with fractions.

Arithmetic facts
Review and practice of the arithmetic facts is still important. This can be done a couple of times per week both orally and written (e.g. with our arithmetic fact speed sheets).

Games for lower classes maths

All of the following games are related to maths.*

It is fun for the students to experience the world of numbers in a playful way. All these games can be used from Class Two and up.

Our puzzle and game book

There may be times when the teacher knows it is time to do something different. Randy Evans' book, *Fun with Puzzles, Games and More,* is intended as a resource for maths teachers in Classes Four to Twelve, in part to supplement the normal classroom material. It provides ideas for that 'something different'.

Dominoes games (there is a great variety)
- Krypto card games
- Numbers factory

Bingo games (there is a great variety)
- Conceptual bingo with fractions
- Conceptual bingo with decimals
- Conceptual bingo with fractions to decimals

Traditional games

These can help with simple counting, and arithmetic.
- Monopoly
- Yahtzee
- Shut the box
- Can't stop

* Most of these games were found at the Math and Stuff store in Seattle, USA; *www.math-n-stuff.com*. It is a wellspring of maths resources.

Games using the four processes $(+, -, \times, \div)$
- Equate (all star math games)
- Roll 'n multiply (all star math games)
- Smath: the game that makes math fun
- Hands on learning, maths card games
- Math mania highlights

Other ideas
- A box with six maths board games for all ages
- Mind bending puzzles books, by Lagoon Books
- Books with mazes
- Books with patterns

A step-by-step progression for the arithmetic facts

Step 1: Basic rhythmical counting (Class One)
In Class One, rhythmical counting exercises are done with the 2, 3, 4, 5, 10 and 11 times tables.

Step 2: Addition and subtraction facts (Class One & Two)
Starting in Class One with some of the more basic facts (e.g. $5 = 3 + 2$, and $12 = 6 + 6$), the children begin to learn the addition facts, and corresponding subtraction facts, by heart. By the end of Class Two, these more basic facts should be solid with most of the students, and by the end of Class Three, the whole class should have mastered all of the addition and subtraction facts.

Step 3: Basic times/division tables (Class Two): the 2, 3, 4, 5, 10 and 11 times tables

We now build on the rhythmical counting exercises that were done in Class One. In Class Two, we begin to introduce the times/division tables as a concept, in an artistic way. These are introduced through movement in different ways and also written down. We should find ways to integrate the times and division tables together. For example, we can say:

$1 \times 6 = 6, 6 = 1 \times 6, 6 \div 1 = 6;$
$2 \times 6 = 12, 12 = 2 \times 6, 12 \div 2 = 6;$
$3 \times 6 = 18, 18 = 3 \times 6, 18 \div 3 = 6,$ etc.

Step 4: Advanced times/division tables (Class Two): the 6, 7, 8 and 9 times tables

In Class One, rhythmical counting exercises were not done for 6 to 9. Now in Class Two, they can work on the 6 times through to the 9 times table, and the 12 times table as well. In contrast to the rhythmical counting that was done in Class One, the class can jump right into speaking each of these more advanced tables (e.g. with the 6s, we say: '6, 12, 18, 24, 30,' etc.).

Step 5: Individual practice (Class Two)

First, after a times table has been introduced and we have practised the rhythmical sequences of that times table, we then need to have the children practise writing the times and division tables in a row. Each student should be able to write down each times table in a horizontal row without any help.

Step 6: Arithmetic facts (Class Three)

The goal is that, by the end of Class Three, the whole class has learned the arithmetic facts by heart. Our arithmetic facts practice sheets are designed to be done almost daily for 20 weeks. (For more details, see *Arithmetic facts practice sheets*, p. 75) In Class Three, we should also work with remainders (e.g. $20 \div 6 = 3$ r 2).

Step 7: Review and practice (Class Four & Five)

Arithmetic facts practice, review and speed sheets should be done in Classes Four and Five in order to reinforce what has been learned, and to keep it fresh. Two or three sheets per week – each sheet taking only 3 to 5 minutes – should be enough. Daily mental arithmetic also supports this effort.

More on learning the arithmetic facts

There may be a significant overlap between some of the above steps – that is, one step does not necessarily need to be finished with all tables before beginning the next step with another table.

Rhythmical work should continue in Class Three, but we must ensure that it includes sufficient work with the 'head memory'. To do this effectively, we shouldn't only have the students recite the tables together as a class with choral speaking, but we should also call on individual students to give answers to facts out of sequence.

The multiplication facts aren't so numerous. There are a total of 66 multiplication facts, but only 17 of them are 'hard' (these are from the

A Teacher's Source Book for Mathematics in Classes 1 to 5

6, 7, 8, 9 and 12 times tables, plus 11×11 and 11×12). Even if you add in the 4 and 3 times tables, that's only 30 'hard' facts to learn.

Division facts. Starting in Class Two, the division facts should always be done with the multiplication facts. For instance, if you are working on $8 \times 7 = 56$, then at the same time you can do $56 \div 8$, and $56 \div 7$, as well as problems like $8 \times \underline{\quad} = 56$.

The subtraction facts are often not given enough emphasis. In middle school, it is often the subtraction facts (like $12 - 7$) that slow students down the most when doing calculations.

There are 81 subtraction facts to memorise – 45 subtraction facts that are from 10 and under (e.g. $8 - 3$) and 36 'borrowing' facts (e.g. $13 - 8$). Practicing the subtraction facts in Class One to Class Three is very important.

The first 100 square numbers

1^2 is 1	21^2 is 441	41^2 is 1681	61^2 is 3721	81^2 is 6561
2^2 is 4	22^2 is 484	42^2 is 1764	62^2 is 3844	82^2 is 6724
3^2 is 9	23^2 is 529	43^2 is 1849	63^2 is 3969	83^2 is 6889
4^2 is 16	24^2 is 576	44^2 is 1936	64^2 is 4096	84^2 is 7056
5^2 is 25	25^2 is 625	45^2 is 2025	65^2 is 4225	85^2 is 7225
6^2 is 36	26^2 is 676	46^2 is 2116	66^2 is 4356	86^2 is 7396
7^2 is 49	27^2 is 729	47^2 is 2209	67^2 is 4489	87^2 is 7569
8^2 is 64	28^2 is 784	48^2 is 2304	68^2 is 4624	88^2 is 7744
9^2 is 81	29^2 is 841	49^2 is 2401	69^2 is 4761	89^2 is 7921
10^2 is 100	30^2 is 900	50^2 is 2500	70^2 is 4900	90^2 is 8100
11^2 is 121	31^2 is 961	51^2 is 2601	71^2 is 5041	91^2 is 8281
12^2 is 144	32^2 is 1024	52^2 is 2704	72^2 is 5184	92^2 is 8464
13^2 is 169	33^2 is 1089	53^2 is 2809	73^2 is 5329	93^2 is 8649
14^2 is 196	34^2 is 1156	54^2 is 2916	74^2 is 5476	94^2 is 8836
15^2 is 225	35^2 is 1225	55^2 is 3025	75^2 is 5625	95^2 is 9025
16^2 is 256	36^2 is 1296	56^2 is 3136	76^2 is 5776	96^2 is 9216
17^2 is 289	37^2 is 1369	57^2 is 3249	77^2 is 5929	97^2 is 9409
18^2 is 324	38^2 is 1444	58^2 is 3364	78^2 is 6084	98^2 is 9604
19^2 is 361	39^2 is 1521	59^2 is 3481	79^2 is 6241	99^2 is 9801
20^2 is 400	40^2 is 1600	60^2 is 3600	80^2 is 6400	100^2 is 10,000

The first 75 triangular numbers

1 Δ is 1	16 Δ is 136	31 Δ is 496	46 Δ is 1081	61 Δ is 1891
2 Δ is 3	17 Δ is 153	32 Δ is 528	47 Δ is 1128	62 Δ is 1953
3 Δ is 6	18 Δ is 171	33 Δ is 561	48 Δ is 1176	63 Δ is 2016
4 Δ is 10	19 Δ is 190	34 Δ is 595	49 Δ is 1225	64 Δ is 2080
5 Δ is 15	20 Δ is 210	35 Δ is 630	50 Δ is 1275	65 Δ is 2145
6 Δ is 21	21 Δ is 231	36 Δ is 666	51 Δ is 1326	66 Δ is 2211
7 Δ is 28	22 Δ is 253	37 Δ is 703	52 Δ is 1378	67 Δ is 2278
8 Δ is 36	23 Δ is 276	38 Δ is 741	53 Δ is 1431	68 Δ is 2346
9 Δ is 45	24 Δ is 300	39 Δ is 780	54 Δ is 1485	69 Δ is 2415
10 Δ is 55	25 Δ is 325	40 Δ is 820	55 Δ is 1540	70 Δ is 2485
11 Δ is 66	26 Δ is 351	41 Δ is 861	56 Δ is 1596	71 Δ is 2556
12 Δ is 78	27 Δ is 378	42 Δ is 903	57 Δ is 1653	72 Δ is 2628
13 Δ is 91	28 Δ is 406	43 Δ is 946	58 Δ is 1711	73 Δ is 2701
14 Δ is 105	29 Δ is 435	44 Δ is 990	59 Δ is 1770	74 Δ is 2775
15 Δ is 120	30 Δ is 465	45 Δ is 1035	60 Δ is 1830	75 Δ is 2850

Perfect, abundant and deficient numbers

The abundance quotient is the sum of its factors (except for the number itself) divided by the number itself. For example, with 24, the sum of its factors is 36, so the abundance quotient for 24 is $36 \div 24 = 1.5$.

All *perfect numbers*, by definition, have an abundance quotient exactly equal to one. The first nine perfect numbers are:

6   28   496
8128   33,550,336   8,589,869,056
137,438,691,328
2,305,843,008,139,952,128
2,658,455,991,569,831,744,654,692,615,953,842,176

The tenth perfect number has 54 digits! It is still unknown if any odd perfect number exists.

Interestingly, the first 231 *abundant numbers* are all even numbers. The first odd-numbered abundant number is 945 (quotient = 1.032), and the second one is 1575 (quotient = 1.047). The abundance quotients of each of the 'biggest' abundant numbers (i.e. having an abundance quotient greater than any previous number) from 6 up to 30,000 are listed opposite.

12 is abundant with a quotient of 1.333

24 is abundant with a quotient of 1.500

36 is abundant with a quotient of 1.528

48 is abundant with a quotient of 1.583

60 is abundant with a quotient of 1.800

120 is abundant with a quotient of 2.000

180 is abundant with a quotient of 2.033

240 is abundant with a quotient of 2.100

360 is abundant with a quotient of 2.250

720 is abundant with a quotient of 2.358

840 is abundant with a quotient of 2.429

1260 is abundant with a quotient of 2.467

1680 is abundant with a quotient of 2.543

2520 is abundant with a quotient of 2.714

5040 is abundant with a quotient of 2.838

10,080 is abundant with a quotient of 2.900

15,120 is abundant with a quotient of 2.937

25,200 is abundant with a quotient of 2.966

27,720 is abundant with a quotient of 3.052

Quotients for abundant numbers up to 150

Here are the abundance quotients for the abundant numbers up to 150:

12 has a quotient of 1.333

18 has a quotient of 1.167

20 has a quotient of 1.100

24 has a quotient of 1.500

28 has a quotient of 1.000

30 has a quotient of 1.400

36 has a quotient of 1.528

40 has a quotient of 1.250

42 has a quotient of 1.286

48 has a quotient of 1.583

54 has a quotient of 1.222

56 has a quotient of 1.143

60 has a quotient of 1.800

66 has a quotient of 1.182

70 has a quotient of 1.057

72 has a quotient of 1.708

78 has a quotient of 1.154

80 has a quotient of 1.325

84 has a quotient of 1.667

88 has a quotient of 1.045

90 has a quotient of 1.600

96 has a quotient of 1.625

100 has a quotient of 1.170

102 has a quotient of 1.118

104 has a quotient of 1.019

108 has a quotient of 1.593

112 has a quotient of 1.214

114 has a quotient of 1.105

120 has a quotient of 2.000

126 has a quotient of 1.476

132 has a quotient of 1.545

138 has a quotient of 1.087

140 has a quotient of 1.400

Powers of two

2^1 is 2

2^2 is 4

2^3 is 8

2^4 is 16

2^5 is 32

2^6 is 64

2^7 is 128

2^8 is 256

2^9 is 512

2^{10} is 1024

2^{11} is 2048

2^{12} is 4096

2^{13} is 8192

2^{14} is 16,384

2^{15} is 32,768

2^{16} is 65,536

2^{17} is 131,072

2^{18} is 262,144

2^{19} is 524,288

2^{20} is 1,048,576

2^{21} is 2,097,152

2^{22} is 4,194,304

2^{23} is 8,388,608

2^{24} is 16,777,216

2^{25} is 33,554,432

2^{26} is 67,108,864

2^{27} is 134,217,728

2^{28} is 268,435,456

2^{29} is 536,870,912

2^{30} is 1,073,741,824

2^{31} is 2,147,483,648

2^{32} is 4,294,967,296

2^{33} is 8,589,934,592

2^{34} is 17,179,869,184

2^{35} is 34,359,738,368

2^{36} is 68,719,476,736

2^{37} is 137,438,953,472

2^{38} is 274,877,906,944

2^{39} is 549,755,813,888

2^{40} is 1,099,511,627,776

2^{41} is 2,199,023,255,552

2^{42} is 4,398,046,511,104

2^{43} is 8,796,093,022,208

2^{44} is 17,592,186,044,416

2^{45} is 35,184,372,088,832

2^{46} is 70,368,744,177,664

2^{47} is 140,737,488,355,328

2^{48} is 281,474,976,710,656

2^{49} is 562,949,953,421,312

2^{50} is 1,125,899,906,842,624

2^{51} is 2,251,799,813,685,248

2^{52} is 4,503,599,627,370,496

2^{53} is 9,007,199,254,740,992

2^{54} is 18,014,398,509,481,984

2^{55} is 36,028,797,018,963,968

2^{56} is 72,057,594,037,927,936

2^{57} is 144,115,188,075,855,872

2^{58} is 288,230,376,151,711,744

2^{59} is 576,460,752,303,423,488

2^{60} is 1,152,921,504,606,846,976

2^{61} is 2,305,843,009,213,693,952

2^{62} is 4,611,686,018,427,387,904

2^{63} is 9,223,372,036,854,775,808

2^{64} is 18,446,744,073,709,551,616

2^{65} is 36,893,488,147,419,103,232

2^{66} is 73,786,976,294,838,206,464

2^{67} is 147,573,952,589,676,412,928

2^{68} is 295,147,905,179,352,825,856
2^{69} is 590,295,810,358,705,651,712
2^{70} is 1,180,591,620,717,411,303,424
2^{71} is 2,361,183,241,434,822,606,848
2^{72} is 4,722,366,482,869,645,213,696
2^{73} is 9,444,732,965,739,290,427,392
2^{74} is 18,889,465,931,478,580,854,784
2^{75} is 37,778,931,862,957,161,709,568
2^{76} is 75,557,863,725,914,323,419,136
2^{77} is 151,115,727,451,828,646,838,272
2^{78} is 302,231,454,903,657,293,676,544
2^{79} is 604,462,909,807,314,587,353,088
2^{80} is 1,208,925,819,614,629,174,706,176
2^{81} is 2,417,851,639,229,258,349,412,352
2^{82} is 4,835,703,278,458,516,698,824,704
2^{83} is 9,671,406,556,917,033,397,649,408
2^{84} is 19,342,813,113,834,066,795,298,816
2^{85} is 38,685,626,227,668,133,590,597,632
2^{86} is 77,371,252,455,336,267,181,195,264
2^{87} is 154,742,504,910,672,534,362,390,528
2^{88} is 309,485,009,821,345,068,724,781,056
2^{89} is 618,970,019,642,690,137,449,562,112
2^{90} is 1,237,940,039,285,380,274,899,124,224
2^{91} is 2,475,880,078,570,760,549,798,248,448
2^{92} is 4,951,760,157,141,521,099,596,496,896
2^{93} is 9,903,520,314,283,042,199,192,993,792
2^{94} is 19,807,040,628,566,084,398,385,987,584
2^{95} is 39,614,081,257,132,168,796,771,975,168
2^{96} is 79,228,162,514,264,337,593,543,950,336
2^{97} is 158,456,325,028,528,675,187,087,900,672
2^{98} is 316,912,650,057,057,350,374,175,801,344
2^{99} is 633,825,300,114,114,700,748,351,602,688
2^{100} is 1,267,650,600,228,229,401,496,703,205,376

Prime numbers up to 2000

2	139	331
3	149	337
5	151	347
7	157	349
11	163	353
13	167	359
17	173	367
19	179	373
23	181	379
29	191	383
31	193	389
37	197	397
41	199	401
43	211	409
47	223	419
53	227	421
59	229	431
61	233	433
67	239	439
71	241	443
73	251	449
79	257	457
83	263	461
89	269	463
97	271	467
101	277	479
103	281	487
107	283	491
109	293	499
113	307	503
127	311	509
131	313	521
137	317	523

541	757	997	1231	1487	1733
547	761	1009	1237	1489	1741
557	769	1013	1249	1493	1747
563	773	1019	1259	1499	1753
569	787	1021	1277	1511	1759
571	797	1031	1279	1523	1777
577	809	1033	1283	1531	1783
587	811	1039	1289	1543	1787
593	821	1049	1291	1549	1789
599	823	1051	1297	1553	1801
601	827	1061	1301	1559	1811
607	829	1063	1303	1567	1823
613	839	1069	1307	1571	1831
617	853	1087	1319	1579	1847
619	857	1091	1321	1583	1861
631	859	1093	1327	1597	1867
641	863	1097	1361	1601	1871
643	877	1103	1367	1607	1873
647	881	1109	1373	1609	1877
653	883	1117	1381	1613	1879
659	887	1123	1399	1619	1889
661	907	1129	1409	1621	1901
673	911	1151	1423	1627	1907
677	919	1153	1427	1637	1913
683	929	1163	1429	1657	1931
691	937	1171	1433	1663	1933
701	941	1181	1439	1667	1949
709	947	1187	1447	1669	1951
719	953	1193	1451	1693	1973
727	967	1201	1453	1697	1979
733	971	1213	1459	1699	1987
739	977	1217	1471	1709	1993
743	983	1223	1481	1721	1997
751	991	1229	1483	1723	1999

A Teacher's Source Book for Mathematics in Classes 1 to 5

Even numbers as the sum of two primes

 4 = 2+2

 6 = 3+3

 8 = 3+5

10 = 3+7; 5+5

12 = 5+7

14 = 3+11; 7+7

16 = 3+13; 5+11

18 = 5+13; 7+11

20 = 3+17; 7+13

22 = 3+19; 5+17; 11+11

24 = 5+19; 7+17; 11+13

26 = 3+23; 7+19; 13+13

28 = 5+23; 11+17

30 = 7+23; 11+19; 13+17

32 = 3+29; 13+19

34 = 3+31; 5+29; 11+23; 17+17

36 = 5+31; 7+29; 13+23; 17+19

38 = 7+31; 19+19

40 = 3+37; 11+29; 17+23

42 = 5+37; 11+31; 13+29; 19+23

44 = 3+41; 7+37; 13+31

46 = 3+43; 5+41; 17+29; 23+23

48 = 5+43; 7+41; 11+37; 17+31; 19+29

50 = 3+47; 7+43; 13+37; 19+31

52 = 5+47; 11+41; 23+29

54 = 7+47; 11+43; 13+41; 17+37; 23+31

56 = 3+53; 13+43; 19+37

58 = 5+53; 11+47; 17+41; 29+29

60 = 7+53; 13+47; 17+43; 19+41; 23+37; 29+31

62 = 3+59; 19+43; 31+31

64 = 3+61; 5+59; 11+53; 17+47; 23+41

66 = 5+61; 7+59; 13+53; 19+47; 23+43; 29+37

68 = 7+61; 31+37

70 = 3+67; 11+59; 17+53; 23+47; 29+41

72 = 5+67; 11+61; 13+59; 19+53; 29+43; 31+41

74 = 3+71; 7+67; 13+61; 31+43; 37+37

76 = 3+73; 5+71; 17+59; 23+53; 29+47

78 = 5+73; 7+71; 11+67; 17+61; 19+59; 31+47; 37+41

80 = 7+73; 13+67; 19+61; 37+43

82 = 3+79; 11+71; 23+59; 29+53; 41+41

84 = 5+79; 11+73; 13+71; 17+67; 23+61; 31+53; 37+47; 41+43

86 = 3+83; 7+79; 13+73; 19+67; 43+43

88 = 5+83; 17+71; 29+59; 41+47

90 = 7+83; 11+79; 17+73; 19+71; 23+67; 29+61; 31+59; 37+53; 43+47

92 = 3+89; 13+79; 19+73; 31+61

94 = 5+89; 11+83; 23+71; 41+53; 47+47

96 = 7+89; 13+83; 17+79; 23+73; 29+67; 37+59; 43+53
 98 = 19+79; 31+67; 37+61
100 = 3+97; 11+89; 17+83; 29+71; 41+59; 47+53
102 = 5+97; 13+89; 19+83; 23+79; 29+73; 31+71; 41+61; 43+59
104 = 3+101; 7+97; 31+73; 37+67; 43+61
106 = 3+103; 5+101; 17+89; 23+83; 47+59; 53+53
108 = 5+103; 7+101; 11+97; 19+89; 29+79; 37+71; 41+67; 47+61
110 = 3+107; 7+103; 13+97; 31+79; 37+73; 43+67
112 = 3+109; 5+107; 11+101; 23+89; 29+83; 41+71; 53+59
114 = 5+109; 7+107; 11+103; 13+101; 17+97; 31+83; 41+73; 43+71; 47+67; 53+61
116 = 3+113; 7+109; 13+103; 19+97; 37+79; 43+73
118 = 5+113; 11+107; 17+101; 29+89; 47+71; 59+59
120 = 7+113; 11+109; 13+107; 17+103; 19+101; 23+97; 31+89; 37+83; 41+79; 47+73;
       53+67; 59+61
122 = 13+109; 19+103; 43+79; 61+61
124 = 11+113; 17+107; 23+101; 41+83; 53+71
126 = 13+113; 17+109; 19+107; 23+103; 29+97; 37+89; 43+83; 47+79; 53+73; 59+67
128 = 19+109; 31+97; 61+67
130 = 3+127; 17+113; 23+107; 29+101; 41+89; 47+83; 59+71
132 = 5+127; 19+113; 23+109; 29+103; 31+101; 43+89; 53+79; 59+73; 61+71
134 = 3+131; 7+127; 31+103; 37+97; 61+73; 67+67
136 = 5+131; 23+113; 29+107; 47+89; 53+83
138 = 7+131; 11+127; 29+109; 31+107; 37+101; 41+97; 59+79; 67+71
140 = 3+137; 13+127; 31+109; 37+103; 43+97; 61+79; 67+73
142 = 3+139; 5+137; 11+131; 29+113; 41+101; 53+89; 59+83; 71+71
144 = 5+139; 7+137; 13+131; 17+127; 31+113; 37+107; 41+103; 43+101; 47+97;
       61+83; 71+73
146 = 7+139; 19+127; 37+109; 43+103; 67+79; 73+73
148 = 11+137; 17+131; 41+107; 47+101; 59+89
150 = 11+139; 13+137; 19+131; 23+127; 37+113; 41+109; 43+107; 47+103; 53+97;
       61+89; 67+83; 71+79

Odd numbers as the difference of two squares

$3 = 2^2 - 1^2$

$5 = 3^2 - 2^2$

$7 = 4^2 - 3^2$

$9 = 5^2 - 4^2$

$11 = 6^2 - 5^2$

$13 = 7^2 - 6^2$

$15 = 4^2 - 1^2; 8^2 - 7^2$

$17 = 9^2 - 8^2$

$19 = 10^2 - 9^2$

$21 = 5^2 - 2^2; 11^2 - 10^2$

$23 = 12^2 - 11^2$

$25 = 13^2 - 12^2$

$27 = 6^2 - 3^2; 14^2 - 13^2$

$29 = 15^2 - 14^2$

$31 = 16^2 - 15^2$

$33 = 7^2 - 4^2; 17^2 - 16^2$

$35 = 6^2 - 1^2; 18^2 - 17^2$

$37 = 19^2 - 18^2$

$39 = 8^2 - 5^2; 20^2 - 19^2$

$41 = 21^2 - 20^2$

$43 = 22^2 - 21^2$

$45 = 7^2 - 2^2; 9^2 - 6^2; 23^2 - 22^2$

$47 = 24^2 - 23^2$

$49 = 25^2 - 24^2$

$51 = 10^2 - 7^2; 26^2 - 25^2$

$53 = 27^2 - 26^2$

$55 = 8^2 - 3^2; 28^2 - 27^2$

$57 = 11^2 - 8^2; 29^2 - 28^2$

$59 = 30^2 - 29^2$

$61 = 31^2 - 30^2$

$63 = 8^2 - 1^2; 12^2 - 9^2; 32^2 - 31^2$

$65 = 9^2 - 4^2; 33^2 - 32^2$

$67 = 34^2 - 33^2$

$69 = 13^2 - 10^2; 35^2 - 34^2$

$71 = 36^2 - 35^2$

$73 = 37^2 - 36^2$

$75 = 10^2 - 5^2; 14^2 - 11^2; 38^2 - 37^2$

$77 = 9^2 - 2^2; 39^2 - 38^2$

$79 = 40^2 - 39^2$

$81 = 15^2 - 12^2; 41^2 - 40^2$

$83 = 42^2 - 41^2$

$85 = 11^2 - 6^2; 43^2 - 42^2$

$87 = 16^2 - 13^2; 44^2 - 43^2$

$89 = 45^2 - 44^2$

$91 = 10^2 - 3^2; 46^2 - 45^2$

$93 = 17^2 - 14^2; 47^2 - 46^2$

$95 = 12^2 - 7^2; 48^2 - 47^2$

$97 = 49^2 - 48^2$

$99 = 10^2 - 1^2; 18^2 - 15^2; 50^2 - 49^2$

$101 = 51^2 - 50^2$

$103 = 52^2 - 51^2$

$105 = 11^2 - 4^2; 13^2 - 8^2; 19^2 - 16^2; 53^2 - 52^2$

$107 = 54^2 - 53^2$

$109 = 55^2 - 54^2$

$111 = 20^2 - 17^2; 56^2 - 55^2$

$113 = 57^2 - 56^2$

$115 = 14^2 - 9^2; 58^2 - 57^2$

$117 = 11^2 - 2^2; 21^2 - 18^2; 59^2 - 58^2$

$119 = 12^2 - 5^2; 60^2 - 59^2$

$121 = 61^2 - 60^2$

$123 = 22^2 - 19^2; 62^2 - 61^2$

$125 = 15^2 - 10^2; 63^2 - 62^2$

$127 = 64^2 - 63^2$

$129 = 23^2 - 20^2; 65^2 - 64^2$

$131 = 66^2 - 65^2$

$133 = 13^2 - 6^2; 67^2 - 66^2$

$135 = 12^2 - 3^2; 16^2 - 11^2; 24^2 - 21^2; 68^2 - 67^2$

$137 = 69^2 - 68^2$

$139 = 70^2 - 69^2$

$141 = 25^2 - 22^2; 71^2 - 70^2$

$143 = 12^2 - 1^2; 72^2 - 71^2$

$145 = 17^2 - 12^2; 73^2 - 72^2$

$147 = 14^2 - 7^2; 26^2 - 23^2; 74^2 - 73^2$

$149 = 75^2 - 74^2$

$151 = 76^2 - 75^2$

$153 = 13^2 - 4^2; 27^2 - 24^2; 77^2 - 76^2$

$155 = 18^2 - 13^2; 78^2 - 77^2$

$157 = 79^2 - 78^2$

$159 = 28^2 - 25^2; 80^2 - 79^2$

$161 = 15^2 - 8^2; 81^2 - 80^2$

$163 = 82^2 - 81^2$

$165 = 13^2 - 2^2; 19^2 - 14^2; 29^2 - 26^2; 83^2 - 82^2$

$167 = 84^2 - 83^2$

$169 = 85^2 - 84^2$

$171 = 14^2 - 5^2; 30^2 - 27^2; 86^2 - 85^2$

$173 = 87^2 - 86^2$

$175 = 16^2 - 9^2; 20^2 - 15^2; 88^2 - 87^2$

$177 = 31^2 - 28^2; 89^2 - 88^2$

$179 = 90^2 - 89^2$

$181 = 91^2 - 90^2$

$183 = 32^2 - 29^2; 92^2 - 91^2$

$185 = 21^2 - 16^2; 93^2 - 92^2$

$187 = 14^2 - 3^2; 94^2 - 93^2$

$189 = 15^2 - 6^2; 17^2 - 10^2; 33^2 - 30^2; 95^2 - 94^2$

$191 = 96^2 - 95^2$

$193 = 97^2 - 96^2$

$195 = 14^2 - 1^2; 22^2 - 17^2; 34^2 - 31^2; 98^2 - 97^2$

$197 = 99^2 - 98^2$

$199 = 100^2 - 99^2$

Numbers as the sum of two squares

Numbers that are missing cannot be expressed as the sum of two squares.

$2 = 1^2 + 1^2$

$5 = 1^2 + 2^2$

$8 = 2^2 + 2^2$

$10 = 1^2 + 3^2$

$13 = 2^2 + 3^2$

$17 = 1^2 + 4^2$

$18 = 3^2 + 3^2$

$20 = 2^2 + 4^2$

$25 = 3^2 + 4^2$

$26 = 1^2 + 5^2$

$29 = 2^2 + 5^2$

$32 = 4^2 + 4^2$

$34 = 3^2 + 5^2$

$37 = 1^2 + 6^2$

$40 = 2^2 + 6^2$

$41 = 4^2 + 5^2$

$45 = 3^2 + 6^2$

$50 = 1^2 + 7^2; 5^2 + 5^2$

$52 = 4^2 + 6^2$

$53 = 2^2 + 7^2$

$58 = 3^2 + 7^2$

$61 = 5^2 + 6^2$

$65 = 1^2 + 8^2; 4^2 + 7^2$

$68 = 2^2 + 8^2$

$72 = 6^2 + 6^2$

$73 = 3^2 + 8^2$

$74 = 5^2 + 7^2$

$80 = 4^2 + 8^2$

$82 = 1^2 + 9^2$

$85 = 2^2 + 9^2; 6^2 + 7^2$

A Teacher's Source Book for Mathematics in Classes 1 to 5

$89 = 5^2 + 8^2$

$90 = 3^2 + 9^2$

$97 = 4^2 + 9^2$

$98 = 7^2 + 7^2$

$100 = 6^2 + 8^2$

$101 = 1^2 + 10^2$

$104 = 2^2 + 10^2$

$106 = 5^2 + 9^2$

$109 = 3^2 + 10^2$

$113 = 7^2 + 8^2$

$116 = 4^2 + 10^2$

$117 = 6^2 + 9^2$

$122 = 1^2 + 11^2$

$125 = 2^2 + 11^2; 5^2 + 10^2$

$128 = 8^2 + 8^2$

$130 = 3^2 + 11^2; 7^2 + 9^2$

$136 = 6^2 + 10^2$

$137 = 4^2 + 11^2$

$145 = 1^2 + 12^2; 8^2 + 9^2$

$146 = 5^2 + 11^2$

$148 = 2^2 + 12^2$

$149 = 7^2 + 10^2$

$153 = 3^2 + 12^2$

$157 = 6^2 + 11^2$

$160 = 4^2 + 12^2$

$162 = 9^2 + 9^2$

$164 = 8^2 + 10^2$

$169 = 5^2 + 12^2$

$170 = 1^2 + 13^2; 7^2 + 11^2$

$173 = 2^2 + 13^2$

$178 = 3^2 + 13^2$

$180 = 6^2 + 12^2$

$181 = 9^2 + 10^2$

$185 = 4^2 + 13^2; 8^2 + 11^2$

$193 = 7^2 + 12^2$

$194 = 5^2 + 13^2$

$197 = 1^2 + 14^2$

$200 = 2^2 + 14^2; 10^2 + 10^2$

$202 = 9^2 + 11^2$

$205 = 3^2 + 14^2; 6^2 + 13^2$

$208 = 8^2 + 12^2$

$212 = 4^2 + 14^2$

$218 = 7^2 + 13^2$

$221 = 5^2 + 14^2; 10^2 + 11^2$

$225 = 9^2 + 12^2$

$226 = 1^2 + 15^2$

$229 = 2^2 + 15^2$

$232 = 6^2 + 14^2$

$233 = 8^2 + 13^2$

$234 = 3^2 + 15^2$

$241 = 4^2 + 15^2$

$242 = 11^2 + 11^2$

$244 = 10^2 + 12^2$

$245 = 7^2 + 14^2$

$250 = 5^2 + 15^2; 9^2 + 13^2$

$257 = 1^2 + 16^2$

$260 = 2^2 + 16^2; 8^2 + 14^2$

$261 = 6^2 + 15^2$

$265 = 3^2 + 16^2; 11^2 + 12^2$

$269 = 10^2 + 13^2$

$272 = 4^2 + 16^2$

$274 = 7^2 + 15^2$

$277 = 9^2 + 14^2$

$281 = 5^2 + 16^2$

$288 = 12^2 + 12^2$

$289 = 8^2 + 15^2$

$290 = 1^2 + 17^2; 11^2 + 13^2$

$292 = 6^2 + 16^2$

$293 = 2^2 + 17^2$

$296 = 10^2 + 14^2$

298 $= 3^2 + 17^2$

305 $= 4^2 + 17^2; 7^2 + 16^2$

306 $= 9^2 + 15^2$

313 $= 12^2 + 13^2$

314 $= 5^2 + 17^2$

317 $= 11^2 + 14^2$

320 $= 8^2 + 16^2$

325 $= 1^2 + 18^2; 6^2 + 17^2; 10^2 + 15^2$

328 $= 2^2 + 18^2$

333 $= 3^2 + 18^2$

337 $= 9^2 + 16^2$

338 $= 7^2 + 17^2; 13^2 + 13^2$

340 $= 4^2 + 18^2; 12^2 + 14^2$

346 $= 11^2 + 15^2$

349 $= 5^2 + 18^2$

353 $= 8^2 + 17^2$

356 $= 10^2 + 16^2$

360 $= 6^2 + 18^2$

362 $= 1^2 + 19^2$

365 $= 2^2 + 19^2; 13^2 + 14^2$

369 $= 12^2 + 15^2$

370 $= 3^2 + 19^2; 9^2 + 17^2$

373 $= 7^2 + 18^2$

377 $= 4^2 + 19^2; 11^2 + 16^2$

386 $= 5^2 + 19^2$

388 $= 8^2 + 18^2$

389 $= 10^2 + 17^2$

392 $= 14^2 + 14^2$

394 $= 13^2 + 15^2$

397 $= 6^2 + 19^2$

400 $= 12^2 + 16^2$

401 $= 1^2 + 20^2$

404 $= 2^2 + 20^2$

405 $= 9^2 + 18^2$

409 $= 3^2 + 20^2$

410 $= 7^2 + 19^2; 11^2 + 17^2$

416 $= 4^2 + 20^2$

421 $= 14^2 + 15^2$

424 $= 10^2 + 18^2$

425 $= 5^2 + 20^2; 8^2 + 19^2; 13^2 + 16^2$

433 $= 12^2 + 17^2$

436 $= 6^2 + 20^2$

442 $= 1^2 + 21^2; 9^2 + 19^2$

The first number that can be expressed in 4 ways is

1,105 $= 4^2 + 33^2; 9^2 + 32^2; 12^2 + 31^2;$
$23^2 + 24^2$

Suggested Reading

Anderson, Henning, *Active Arithmetic! Movement and Mathematics Teaching in the Lower Grades of a Waldorf School,* Waldorf Publications, USA, 1995.

Baravalle, Herman von, *The Teaching of Arithmetic and the Waldorf School Plan,* Rudolf Steiner College Publications, USA, 1991.

Bockemühl, Jochen (ed.), *Towards a Phenomenology of the Etheric World,* Anthroposophic Press, USA, 1985.

Diggins, Julia E. *String, Straight Edge and Shadow,* Jamie York Press, USA, 2012.

Evans, Randy; Mick Follari & Jamie York, *Fun with Puzzles, Games and More!,* Jamie York Press, USA, 2012.

Gardner, Howard, *Five Minds for the Future,* Harvard Business School, 2009.

Göttgens, Else, *Waldorf Education in Practice: Exploring How Children Learn in the Lower Grades,* Outskirts Press, USA, 2011.

Groh, Irene & Mona Ruef, *Education and Teaching as Preventive Medicine,* Verlag am Goetheanum, Switzerland, 2006.

Grouws, D.A. (ed.), *Handbook of Research on Mathematics Teaching and Learning,* Macmillan, USA, 1992.

Harrer, Dorothy, *Math Lessons For Elementary Grades,* AWSNA Publications, USA, 2005.

Jaffke, Christoph, *Rhythms, Rhymes, Games and Songs for the Lower School,* Pädagogische Forschungstelle, Bund der Freien Waldorf Schulen, Stuttgart, Germany, 2001.

Jarman, Ron, *Teaching Mathematics in Rudolf Steiner Schools for Classes I–VIII,* Hawthorn Press, UK, 1998.

Kohn, Alfie, *The Homework Myth: Why our Kids Get too Much of a Bad Thing,* Da Capo, USA, 2007.

Ma, Lipping, *Knowing and Teaching Elementary Mathematics: Teachers' Understanding of Fundamental Mathematics in China and the United States,* Routledge, USA, 2010.

Schuberth, Ernst, *Geometry Lessons in the Waldorf School,* Volume 2, AWSNA Publications, USA, 2004.

—, *Teaching Mathematics for First and Second Grades in Waldorf Schools,* Rudolf Steiner College Press, USA, 1999.

Steiner, Rudolf, *The Being of Man and His Future Evolution,* Rudolf Steiner Press, UK, 1981.

—, *The Child's Changing Consciousness,* Anthroposophic Press, USA, 1996.

—, *The Destinies of Individuals and of Nations,* Anthropsophic Press, USA, 1990.

—, *The Education of the Child in the Light of Anthroposophy,* Anthroposophic Press, USA, 1998.

—, *The Foundations of Human Experience,* Anthroposophic Press, USA, 1985.

—, *Human Values in Education,* SteinerBooks, USA, 2005.

—, *The Kingdom of Childhood,* Anthroposophic Press, USA, 1995.

—, *Renewal of Education,* SteinerBooks, USA, 2001.

—, *Spiritual Ground of Education,* SteinerBooks, USA, 2004.

Tahan, Malba, *The Man Who Counted: A Collection of Mathematical Adventures,* W.W. Norton, New York & London, 2015.

Thomas, Heather, *A Journey Through Time in Verse and Rhyme,* Floris Books, 1987.

Walle, John A. van de, *Elementary and Middle School Mathematics,* Longman, USA, 1994.

Index

A Teacher's Source Book for Mathematics in Classes 1 to 5

MAKING MATHS
MEANINGFUL

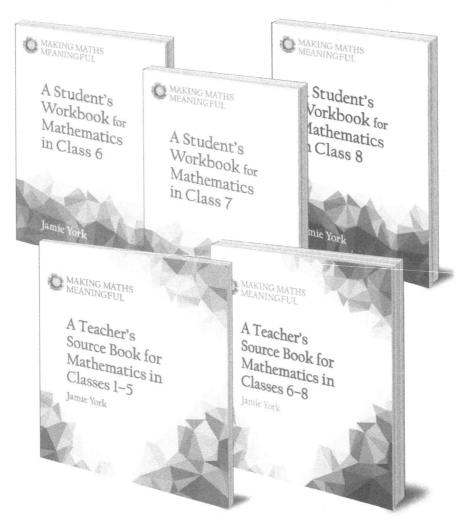

Jamie York's unique maths books are available for Classes 1 to 8, with two comprehensive teacher's source books plus separate student workbooks for Classes 6, 7 and 8. Workbooks are available individually or in classroom packs with a teacher's answer booklet.

"Jamie York has helped me develop students who are on the path to becoming imaginative, analytical thinkers in high school."
– Waldorf teacher, Portland, Oregon

florisbooks.co.uk